Albany N.Y 12203 459-2954

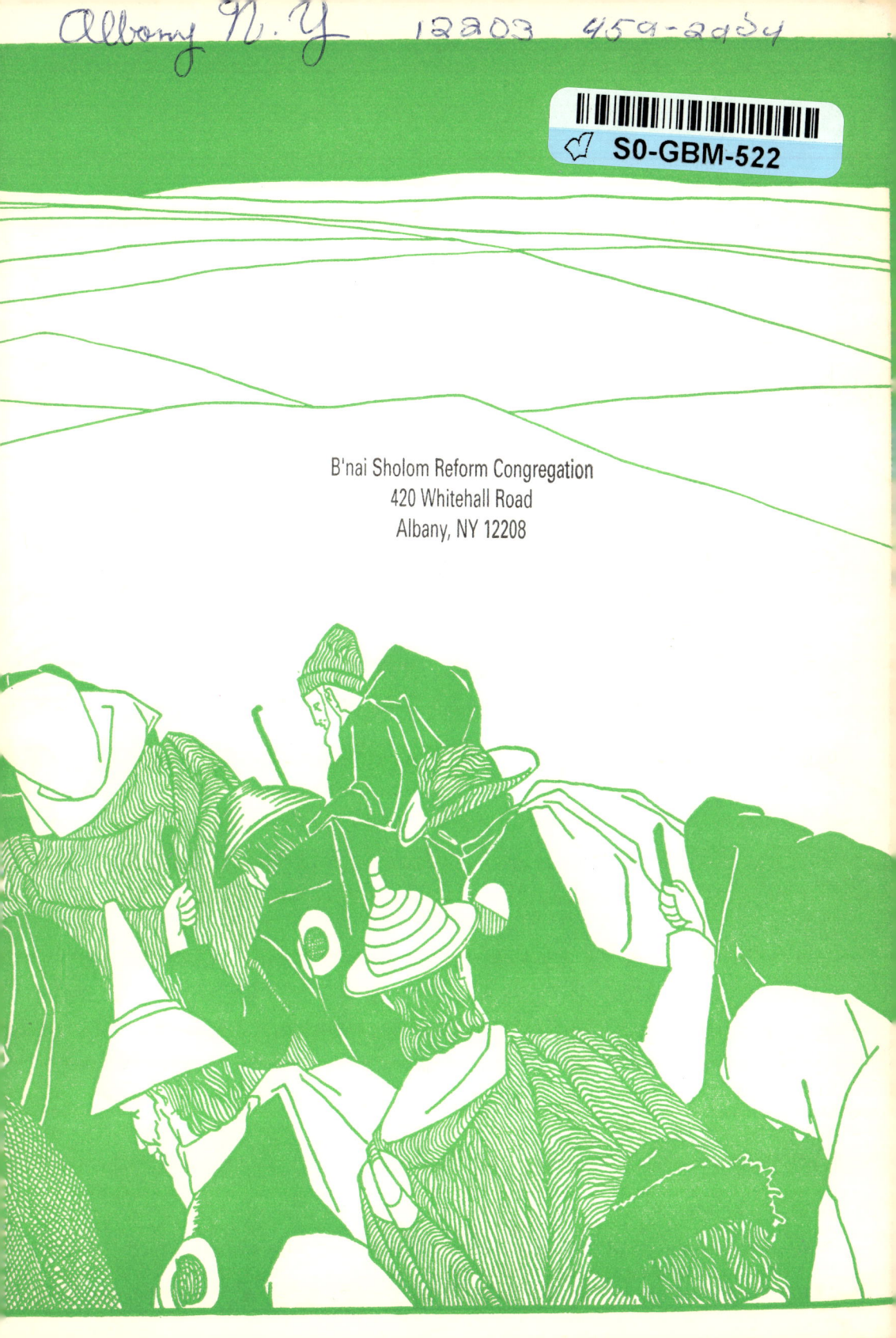

B'nai Sholom Reform Congregation
420 Whitehall Road
Albany, NY 12208

THE
GREAT MARCH
BOOK I

COMMISSION ON
JEWISH EDUCATION
of the UNION OF AMERICAN HEBREW CONGREGATIONS
and CENTRAL CONFERENCE OF AMERICAN RABBIS
AS OF 1966

ROLAND B. GITTELSOHN, *Chairman*
JACOB P. RUDIN, *Vice-Chairman*
SOLOMON B. FREEHOF, *Honorary Chairman*

MEMBERS

BERNARD J. BAMBERGER	ALBERT M. LEWIS
ALAN D. BENNETT	JACOB R. MARCUS
MAX O. BERMAN	MORTIMER MAY
MORTON BOTEL	SAMUEL A. NEMZOFF
DAVID I. CEDARBAUM	MARTIN S. ROZENBERG
LEON FRAM	STEPHEN A. SCHAFER
MAX FRANKEL	LAWRENCE W. SCHWARTZ
SAMUEL GLASNER	SYLVAN D. SCHWARTZMAN
DAVID S. HACHEN	MAX A. SHAPIRO
JOSEPH HARLAM	HAROLD SILVER
ABRAHAM J. KLAUSNER	MRS. M. M. SINGER
BERNARD KLIGFELD	ROBERT SPERBER
LEON KRONISH	PAUL M. STEINBERG
	EDWARD ZERIN

MAURICE N. EISENDRATH, *Secretary*
Ex-Officio

SIDNEY L. REGNER   JACOB J. WEINSTEIN

UNION GRADED SERIES
EDITED BY
RABBI ALEXANDER M. SCHINDLER, *Director of Education*
UNION OF AMERICAN HEBREW CONGREGATIONS

CHAIM I. ETROG, *Director of Adult Education*
ABRAHAM SEGAL, *Director of Teacher Education*

THE GREAT MARCH

Post-Biblical Jewish Stories

BOOK I

BY ROSE G. LURIE

Illustrations by Todros Geller

THE UNION OF AMERICAN HEBREW CONGREGATIONS

NEW YORK, MCMXXXI

COPYRIGHT, 1931, BY
THE UNION OF AMERICAN HEBREW CONGREGATIONS

Nineteenth Printing, 1966

PRINTED IN THE UNITED STATES OF AMERICA

To

AVI AMOS

EDITOR'S INTRODUCTION

The Great March represents a selection of Jewish stories for little children covering the period beginning with the Destruction of the First Temple and ending with the expulsion from Spain. As the book is intended to meet the needs of children in Grades Three or Four, the stories are written in simple style. A definite attempt was made by the author to write the stories as they would be told to the child by the teacher in the class or by the mother in the home. It is important that those using the book should bear this in mind. It will help them to make adequate use of the story material presented.

Too often stories in books intended for little children are abbreviated and condensed, the writers being under a mistaken impression that an abbreviated story shortened from a more expanded narrative for adults constitutes a good story for children. Actually, children need more details, more vivid and concrete writing. So the stories in this book were written especially in conversational tone, and the concreteness and vividness with which they are told should render them easy for dramatization. For this reason, too, the language, the style, and the sentence structure follow essentially the rule of simplicity.

It is well for teachers using this book to remember that the chief aim in teaching Jewish stories of the Post-Biblical Period to children in the early grades is not so much to convey information as to give inspiration. The cultivation of favorable Jewish attitudes is one of the most important aims in any such course of instruction. Whatever information the children may obtain should be considered quite incidental. While we expect them, as a result of study of this book, to know some outstanding Jewish names and some important Jewish events, the primary end is that of cultivating a love for Jewish heroes, for the Jewish people, and for Jewish idealism.

Since the book was not written as a history, it was not deemed necessary to include certain historical events which, though significant, ought not to be included in a book for little children. In other words, good teaching practice at times dictated the omission of some events and some stories. Likewise, the arrangement of the stories, it was thought, need not necessarily be strictly chronological. So, though for the most part the chronological arrangement is maintained, the author departed from it whenever, for psychological reasons, it was deemed advisable to do so.

The author of this book has had years of experience as a teacher and as a critic-teacher, especially in charge of extra-curricular activities in the schools of the Associated Talmud Torahs of Philadelphia. Many of the stories included in this book were tried out experimentally for two or three years with children in the younger grades.

The Union of American Hebrew Congregations sincerely hopes that this book will help meet the needs of our schools, especially in the primary grades. Suggestions and criticisms will be welcomed both by the author and by the editor. If the book should help some of our little boys and girls to develop a love for their people and its ideals, we shall all feel amply repaid for our efforts.

EMANUEL GAMORAN

NOTE TO FOURTEENTH PRINTING, REVISED

The response throughout the country to both volumes of *The Great March* has been such as to justify our issuing a revised edition on the occasion of the fourteenth printing of this volume. We took occasion to make some necessary changes. We also felt that in order to retain the interest which we hope the titles of the stories arouse, we would not want to indicate the personality or the topic treated right next to the title. Hence, for the teacher's information, the following is a list of personalities or events portrayed in these stories:

1. The Second Temple; 2. Alexander the Great; 3. Eliezer; 4. Judas Maccabeus; 5. Rabbi Simon ben Shetach; 6. Hillel; 7. Hillel; 8. Hillel; 9. Story of Bar Kamza; 10. Johanan ben Zakkai; 11. The Siege of Jerusalem; 12. Johanan ben Zakkai; 13. Eliezer ben Hyrcanus; 14. Haninah ben Dosah; 15. Akiba; 16. Akiba; 17. Akiba; 18. Rabbi Meir; 19. Rabbi Meir; 20. Samuel Ibn Adijah; 21. Anan ben David; 22. Saadiah Gaon; 23. Hasdai; 24. The Kazars; 25. Moses ben Enoch; 26. Ibn Gabirol; 27. Judah Halevi; 28. Abraham Ibn Ezra; 29. Maimonides; 30. Maimonides; 31. Nachmanides; 32. Rashi; 33. Rashi; 34. Rashi; 35. David Alroy; 36. Abraham Abulafia; 37. The Crusades; 38. Isaac Abravanel.

E.G.

CONTENTS

	PAGE
EDITOR'S INTRODUCTION	vi
1. The Happy Return	1
2. With Peace They Conquer	10
3. Follow Me	18
4. Fight for Right	22
5. Walking between Raindrops	30
6. School on the Roof	35
7. The Bet	40
8. Torah on One Foot	44
9. Two Who Were Wrong	47
10. The School That Saved a People	52
11. Enough for Wash Day	62
12. The Temple in Ruins	65
13. A B C at Twenty-Two	69
14. The Wicked Neighbor	76
15. The Shepherd Rabbi	80
16. The Cock, the Donkey, and the Candle	88

Contents

	PAGE
17. Fish Out of Water	94
18. Guardians of the Torah	99
19. Ki-Tov—'Twas Good	105
20. As Faithful as That	109
21. The Law Is Kind	114
22. Even Though I Lose	122
23. A Gift to the Caliph	126
24. The Choice	131
25. The Slave Rabbi	137
26. The Wondrous Tree	144
27. In the East Is My Heart	153
28. An Angel Did It	160
29. The Doctor Arrives	169
30. Tables Turned	175
31. The Rabbi Wins	184
32. Not for His Crown	191
33. How Rashi Was Saved	196
34. The Fourth Horse	201
35. Flying from the Roofs	206
36. The Messiah Is Coming	212
37. So This Is Your Answer	216
38. Whither—Now?	222

THE GREAT MARCH

BOOK I

THE HAPPY RETURN

Clish, clash, clash!
Troot, toot, too!
Tra, la, la, la!
Boom, boom, boom!

LISTEN to those noises! Do you hear the clash of the swords; and the thump, thump, thump, of the marching soldiers?

And oh! that crying and moaning and wailing!

The Temple, that beautiful building, has fallen. Jerusalem, the holy city, the city which we thought would never, never, be destroyed lies in ruins—a heap of little stones.

Look at the people. They are pale. Their hands tremble. They cannot walk. They escaped the sword of the enemy and now they are dying of hunger and thirst. A little boy cries: "Mamma, mamma, I want something to eat—just a little piece of bread."

"Mamma, mamma, I am thirsty. I want some water. Oh, please give me just one little drink," moans another.

What can their mothers do? They have no bread for their children, they have no water for them.

Nebuchadnezzar, the mighty king, is taking those who are still living, to his own city, Babylon. They must leave their once beautiful city and their wonderful temple, the temple which King Solomon has built, and they must become prisoners—prisoners in a strange land.

Do you see that blind man walking straight into that tree? Yes, he is Zedekiah, the blind Jewish king. The cruel king, Nebuchadnezzar of Babylonia, has placed him at the head of all the people. And now with only their blind king to lead them, the Jews leave their beloved city.

Listen to their mournful chant as they trudge wearily on:

>*Jerusalem the holy,*
>*No more, no more,*
>*Jerusalem the good,*
>*No more, no more,*
>*The Temple, the beautiful*
>*All,—all are gone.*

Thus slowly and sadly they leave Jerusalem.

* * *

MANY years passed. The little children became big men and women. But they never forgot Jerusalem and the Temple. Ceaselessly they worked and worked, and planned and planned, until they were at last able to return to their dear Jerusalem. They then began to rebuild the Temple which Nebuchadnezzar had destroyed. By this time they were old men and women. Even these people who had never seen Jerusalem and the Temple, but had only heard of it from their grandparents wanted to help in the rebuilding of the Temple.

And many were the little boys and girls who pulled loads of stones, carted dirt, and ran errands for the older people. Oh, they helped all they could and never seemed to get tired. They pulled the stones and pulled the stones for many, many miles. They filled one wagon of dirt and rode away with it, and then another wagon and still another wagon. Not until sunset did they leave off working and go home.

I remember two little boys in particular. They were called Sallu and Nob. At the end of the day you could often hear one say to the other, "Sallu, how many stones did you pull over to the Temple today?"

"More than you did, anyway," Nob would sneer.

"Well, I pulled two more than yesterday," Sallu would say, his black eyes sparkling with glee.

"But, how many altogether?"

"Suppose you tell me first."

"Oh, I pulled twenty stones," Nob would say proudly but quietly.

"Well, I'll pull more than that tomorrow."

And so every day they would ask each other how many loads each had taken away and how many stones each had brought. And the little boy who had done more was the happier.

In the meantime, day after day and week after week, the elders were busy collecting gold and silver and fine stones for the Temple.

One day when they were busier than ever before, the Samaritans, who you know were not Jews, came over and said:

"Let us help you build. We too need a temple. We want to pray together with you."

But the Jews loved the Temple so much that they wanted to do everything, every little bit, all by themselves. Do you blame them? So they answered:

"You are not Jews. Why should you do our work? We thank you very much, but we want to do the work ourselves."

For the next few days the Jews, as usual, worked very hard in peace and quiet. Alas! this did not last long. The Samaritans went to the king of the country and said:

"The Jews are building a temple in Jerusalem. The city, too, they are rebuilding. When all their work is done, O King, they will make war against you. Do not let them finish their work."

So the king sent out an order that all work on the Temple should be stopped. The next day the bricklayers stopped laying the bricks, the carpenters stopped sawing the wood, and the children stopped carting the dirt. Everybody stopped working and that little worker, Sallu, said to Nob:

"Some day I am going to fight those Samaritans. I will gather all the children. I will be the captain. Do you want to join the army?"

"Of course, of course," cried Nob, forgetting his rivalry with Sallu and jumping for joy.

But before Sallu had a chance to gather his army, news came that the Jews were once more permitted to take up the work.

8   The Great March

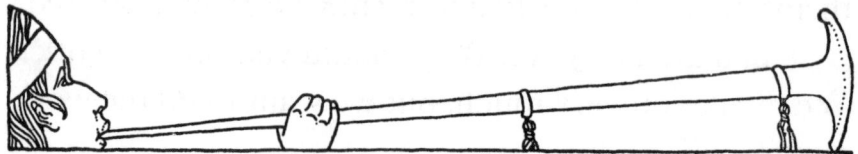

Oh, how happy everybody was! The Temple would at last be finished. But this time they put on their swords. They would take no chances! Now they would be prepared should the Samaritans attack them again. So with sword buckled to belt, each went back to his special task.

Many, many weeks had passed. At last, the great Temple was finished. On a warm summer day, the priests and the singers, the children and all the rest of the people entered the newly built Temple for the first time.

The priests were dressed in long white silk robes. Their jewels shone brightly in the sun as they led the procession into the Temple. Then came the singers dressed in gowns of purple and red, trimmed with gold. After them followed the children, in loose, flowing garments. And who do you think led the children? Why, Sallu and Nob, of course. They had gathered their army but instead of leading it against the Samaritans, they were leading it up, up, up the many stairs to the Temple. Lastly followed the multitude. They all had trumpets and timbrels and harps. At the command of the high priest they began to play their instruments, and sing and shout and dance.

That was indeed a happy day for the Jews. Jerusalem the beloved, the city of David and Solomon, once more had a beautiful Temple. And merrily did the people dance and happily did they sing:

Jerusalem, Jerusalem,
Jerusalem the dear,
Oh how happy, happy
Are we to be here!

Jerusalem, Jerusalem,
Jerusalem the dear,
Oh how happy, happy
Are we to be here!

WITH PEACE THEY CONQUER

WHILE the Jews were busy rebuilding the Temple in Jerusalem, other nations were busy building temples and palaces of their own. One of the nations which had greatly influenced the Jewish people was Macedonia, a country far, far away.

Many years after the Jewish Temple had been finished, a boy was born in that far-off country. This boy was different from most boys. Even as a very young lad, he made up his mind to become king of the whole world. Have you ever known such a boy? Or did you ever know a girl who said, "I'll be queen of the whole world"? Alexander, for that was his name, said, "My father is king of Macedon, but I mean to be king of the whole world."

When he grew up, he was tall and strong. It did not worry him that his left eye was blue and his right

one black. One day an excellent horse was brought to his father, the king. The steed was wild and fiery.

"See what you can do with him," said the king to the chief of his horsemen.

"He—looks—mighty—fierce," said the chief jerkily. And the horse was truly very fierce. The chief of the horsemen could not keep him quiet long enough to mount him. Then another of the king's servants tried. He, too, failed to control the animal. Then Alexander asked if he might try to mount the horse. Everyone was astonished. The king became uneasy, as Alexander leaned his curly yellow head on the horse and stroked him gently. "Take care, he's dangerous," everyone shouted. But to their surprise, Alexander mounted him. The horse stopped jumping and kicking. He was wholly tamed.

This was only one of the brave things Alexander did. When he was twenty years old, he began to war on Thrace and Greece and other countries. He said:

"*Now* I will become king of the whole world."

On one of his campaigns he came to a big Greek temple. In that temple there was an ordinary cart. But on that cart there were knots of heavy, thick ropes. It was believed among the Greeks that the one who untied these knots would surely become king of the world. Many had tried but no one had ever succeeded. Do you think Alexander took a chance? He most certainly did! Boldly, he said to his soldiers:

"Stand by while I try." And walking up quickly to the cart (he always did walk quickly), he began to work on one of the knots. Slowly and patiently he worked away. But still the knot remained unbroken. Then a sudden light flashed from his eyes. Snatching his sword he exclaimed:

"*How* I do it does not matter"—and with one stroke, he cut the knots.

* * *

And Alexander continued to capture city after city and province after province. He became so mighty that he was called Alexander the Great.

One day Alexander sent a troop of soldiers to Jerusalem to get corn and wheat for his city, Tyre.

The Jews were worried. They said:

"If we give corn to Alexander, we shall not be loyal to Persia." So they refused to give either corn or wheat to Alexander's soldiers. The Greek soldiers did not fight with the Jews but went back to Alexander and reported to him their answer.

This naturally made Alexander very, very angry. He called his soldiers together, and said:

"We would have gone up to Jerusalem later. Now

we will go at once. These Jews shall learn that they have no king but Alexander.

"Parmenio! Send out a proclamation that in three days from now Alexander the Great will attack Jerusalem," he commanded.

Can you imagine the fear that came upon the Jews when they received this notice? What would happen to them now? Would they again be driven out of their beloved Jerusalem? Would they have to bow down to strange gods? Would they never be left in peace?

Then Jaddua, the high priest of the Jews, called all the people together.

"Do not fear Alexander. Let us offer up sacrifices and let us pray to our God, the God of Abraham, and no harm will come to us," he said encouragingly, though his voice trembled.

"And then I shall put on my long white priestly robe, and all the priests will do likewise. In addition to this we shall throw flowers on the streets of Jerusalem and deck our houses with all the colored banners we have. We shall meet Alexander as if his coming were a great day,—a great festive day. We shall greet him peacefully, rather than with arms. All will thus be well."

The people looked at one another in silence. They shrugged their shoulders. But no one dared say anything against the advice of the high priest. When they left the Temple, however, they began to grumble.

"I think we shall all be destroyed," said one who looked very wise, and seemed to know all about it.

"Alexander has a big army," said another.

"Yes, even if we did arm ourselves, what could we do against his army?"

"As it is, we may just as well prepare to meet a sure death," said the first.

The three days passed quickly. The streets of Jerusalem looked pretty with all the red, yellow and purple flowers strewn over them. The fragrance, too, was very pleasant. The banners waving from the houses and the Temple added to the festive air. Suddenly the blare of the trumpets was heard. Alexander the Great and his mighty army were approaching. Jaddua, in all his priestly splendor, followed by the priests and people, came forth to meet them. Not a spear, no, not a single ax nor sword could be seen amongst the Jews. "No arms at any price!" was their slogan. "No bloodshed."

The moment Alexander saw the procession he stopped. He was surprised and pleased.

To the amazement of everyone, Alexander the Great, the mighty ruler of more than half the world, bowed down before Jaddua, the Jewish high priest.

What could it mean? How easily he could have conquered them!

"Surely," thought his soldiers, "he must be out of his mind. Think of it, to give up such an easy victory!"

Then Alexander said,

"Come, let us join with the Jews in merrymaking."

He entered the city and together with the high priest offered sacrifices to the God of Israel.

"What has happened to Alexander?" cried his soldiers. "What has happened to Alexander?" cried the Jews.

Wonderful, wonderful! It simply cannot be explained. But Alexander could explain. And he did!

The soldiers and Jews sat down in the Temple. Alexander, who was near the altar, arose and said:

"When I began my march on Jerusalem I thought I would capture it, as I had done all the rest of the cities; but I expected to meet men in full armor, ready for battle."

"We thought so too!" shouted his soldiers. "But if they didn't fight, so much the easier for us."

"I would have killed them all," called a soldier who was bolder than the rest. "Every last one of them," he mumbled, as he clenched his fists and ground his teeth.

"No, my dear man, not at all," said Alexander quietly and calmly.

"When I saw not a spear nor a sword, nor even an ax, I could not raise my hand against them. This is the only people that has met me peacefully instead of with arms. The more glory to their leader, Jaddua, who was brave enough and wise enough to do this."

"Praised be the Lord who helped us do it," said Jaddua, modestly.

A loud cheer arose from the throng.

"Hail to Alexander the Great! All hail to the high priest, Jaddua!"

"Now is there any favor you would ask of me?" said Alexander, kindly.

"Only that we may have our own Jerusalem and that we may worship in our Temple," answered the Jews.

"It is little that you ask. Your prayer shall surely be granted." And Alexander kept his promise.

FOLLOW ME

AFTER many wars, Antiochus became king of Palestine.

Now of all cruel kings he was the most cruel. He wanted all of his subjects to worship one god, the Greek god, Zeus. Troops were sent out all over his kingdom and the people were forced to worship Zeus. They did so because they knew that if they did not obey, they would be killed. But do you think the Jews would give up their one and only God?

One day a band of soldiers returned to Antiochus and reported that all the people in his kingdom had obeyed, except the Jews. Antiochus became red with anger. He seized a beautiful statue that stood near him, threw it to the ground and broke it into tiny bits.

"All the nations under my rule," he cried, "shall sacrifice to one god, and that god shall be Zeus, the god of the Greeks."

The courtiers trembled as Antiochus foamed at the mouth with anger.

"We will send troops there to tear down their altars!"

"And break their holy vessels!" cried the chief general.

"And destroy their walls and gates!" shouted another.

They made quick work of it and were soon setting up Greek altars and Greek idols in the city of Jerusalem.

"Come out—out with you—sacrifice here to Zeus," commands Antiochus the Great.

My, how they hammered away at the doors!

"You, there, you begin. Set an example to the younger ones," growled the Greek general as he dragged the oldest Jew, Eliezer, from the group.

Women and even men began to cry. Oh, how pitiful! How sad! Would Eliezer, the respected ninety-year old man, sacrifice to a strange god?

And what was that? Why, the flesh of swine, dirty swine.

Eliezer, his silvery white hair shining in the sun, was shoved along by the Greeks. When he reached the altar, his strength gave out, and, breathing heavily, he fell to the ground.

"Come now, none of this. Get up and sacrifice the swine to this idol. It's tasty. You will eat some of it afterwards."

The Jews held their breath as Eliezer tried to get up slowly, slowly. On his feet at last, holding on to his staff with one hand, and the altar with the other, he spoke with all the strength he could muster.

"Yes, I will set an example to the younger ones," he said. "Stab me, hang me, burn me,—anything, anything. I will not eat swine nor sacrifice it to your Greek idol."

Some of the Greek soldiers fell on Eliezer and beat him with their swords and spears. The handful of Jews were powerless against the Greeks.

Suddenly amidst all the fury, a piercing shriek was heard from the dying Eliezer:

"Gladly do I die. Thus will the young ones after me learn to fight for their religion."

As he uttered these words, Eliezer fell back and was hushed forever. But there came others who loved their freedom just as much as the faithful Eliezer!

FIGHT FOR RIGHT

"He hit me, he hit me," cried Simon, a little boy with light-brown hair and black eyes. His father, the high priest, came out of the house and looking straight into Simon's eyes asked, "Are you sure that you didn't hit him first?"

"No, no, father," sobbed Simon. "I never hit anyone, though I do wish you hadn't made us promise not to hit. It's awfully hard to keep from hitting back when one is struck for no good reason."

"It's for the best," quietly answered Mattathias, the boy's father.

Simon had four brothers and each one had been taught the same lesson by his father.

Many years had passed since this little incident. The five sons of Mattathias had grown to be big, strong men. Antiochus, the cruel king of Syria, had ordered a regiment of soldiers to go down to the mar-

Fight for Right

ket place. There in the longest and widest street of the city, they built an altar, and on the altar they set up the Greek idol, Zeus. Then the officers went from one Jewish house to another calling:

"Come out, come out and sacrifice to the Greek god. By order of the king, Antiochus, come out!' And the Jews, fearing for their lives, began to gather at the market place.

Now what were the sons of Mattathias to do? Should they offer sacrifices to a Greek idol? If not, they would have to fight the Greeks. And had they not always been taught by their father that they must not fight?

While the Greek soldiers were marching through the town, Mattathias and his sons quickly made their plans. Mattathias, his face lit up by a holy fire, spoke to his sons gently:

"Alas, the time has come when we must fight. Not to fight now would mean to live a life of shame, to be traitors to our faith. We must fight, not for our own lives, not for our own bodies, but for the life of our people. So let us go out, my sons, and let us gather our people together. As many as will be brave enough to go, we will lead to the market place. And then before all the Jews and the Greeks, we will refuse to sacrifice to the idol."

So, while the soldiers were gathering Jews to sacrifice to the idol, Mattathias and his sons were gathering those Jews who were brave enough to refuse.

Before long, the market place was crowded with people, and one of the Greek officers called:

"Who will be the first to sacrifice to the god of the Greeks? Who will set the good example?" One Jew who feared for his life went up to the altar and began to prepare the animal. No sooner had he begun than Mattathias ran up to the coward, snatched the knife from his hand, and killed him. Then waving his sword he called out:

"All those who are for the Law and God, come with me."

A little group of courageous men gathered around him. Together with his five sons, they formed a brave little army.

But they were too few in number to meet the Greeks face to face in open battle. So guess what they did! They hid themselves in the mountains. At night, they would come out of their hiding place and destroy all the altars and idols. When the Greek soldiers pursued them, they would quickly escape to the mountains again. You see, they had to do it that way. Otherwise, the Greeks would surely have killed them. Running in and out of the caves, they soon tore their

clothes. So do you know what they put on for clothes? They had to wear the skins of wild animals to keep from freezing. And they had to eat the meat of the mountain sheep and goats to keep from starving.

They kept this up for a number of months. The long struggle was too much for Mattathias. He died and his five brave sons mourned for their father. Though they were strong and brave, they felt lost without their father. But Judas, who was the strongest, said:

"Of course, our dear father gave us the courage to do everything. But, let us not forget that he asked us to fight for our nation. The way we can best show our love for our father is by fighting to the end."

Judas was chosen leader. And he was glad to have a chance to lead his people. He thought of the great leader, Moses. Oh, how he had always admired Moses! Perhaps, he, Judas, might himself become another Moses!

Antiochus meanwhile was getting more and more cruel. He took away all the golden treasures from the Temple, and placed heathen idols on the altars and set fire to the gates around the temple.

Can you imagine how Judas and his band grieved when they heard that the rough soldiers were shouting and making merry in the Temple, that holy Temple which had been built with so much, so much trouble?

Things were becoming terrible indeed. Judas gave up hiding in the mountains. He and his followers came out and met the Greeks face to face, in a very thrilling battle. I shall tell you all about it.

One night when the Jewish warriors were near Emmaus, Judas said:

"I have a fine plan for a battle. If you will help me carry it out, victory will be ours." The soldiers listened attentively. And Judas continued:

"Half of you will stay here and keep the campfires burning as always. The other half, I will take with me and we will attack the Greeks from the rear. It will be like this:

"The Greeks are in front of you who are left at the camp. They will suspect nothing, since the camp, with its lights, will appear as usual. I shall come up and attack them from behind. So they will be sandwiched between my party in the rear and yours in front of them. Then they will have no way out."

The next day this battle of Emmaus was fought, and Judas' attack turned out just as he had planned. Of course, the Greeks were defeated.

Then loudly and happily, Judas and his army sang:

*Give thanks to the Lord,
For He is good—
His mercy lasts forever.*

*Give thanks to the Lord,
For He is good—
His mercy lasts forever.*

Victorious, the Jews could hardly wait to enter the Temple again. No sooner were they inside than they quickly cast out all the Greek idols and the Greek altars. Then they put back the golden candlesticks, the golden vessels, and all the other sacred things which the Greeks had removed.

When that was finished, they wanted to light the lamp that had always been kept burning in the Temple. But they found only one little bottle of oil. That little bottle could last only one day, and they didn't know how soon they could get more oil. It worried them greatly. But do you know what happened? That little bottle of oil, we are told, lasted eight days instead of one. For eight days there was great merrymaking and rejoicing, and even now we celebrate this holiday called Hanukkah. On this holiday we tell about the wonderful victory which Judas and his little band won over the Greeks and their religion. And every Hanukkah as little Jewish boys and girls light the Hanukkah lights, I can hear them sing:

> *Little candles burning bright,*
> *What do we see in your light?*
> *We see heroes strong and brave,*
> *Who gave their lives, their faith to save.*

WALKING BETWEEN RAINDROPS

AT THE time of Rabbi Simon ben Shetach, there lived eighty witches in a cave.

"That must not be," said Rabbi Simon. "Eighty women just wasting away their time."

One day when the rain was pouring down in torrents, Simon gathered eighty tall young men. To each man he gave a new pitcher. Into this pitcher, each one put a clean new Talis (prayer shawl). Then they turned the pitchers upside down over their heads. In this way, the prayer shawls were kept dry.

Rabbi Simon then said to the young men:

"When we arrive at the cave, this is what you'll do. When I whistle once, put the wraps on; when I whistle again, come into the cave at once. As each of you enters, lift a young woman off the floor. (Once the witches are off the floor, they lose their power.)"

And so they all set out for the cave.

When they reached the cave, the Rabbi knocked at the door and said:

> "*Oo-yim—*
> *Oo-yim,*
> *Open the door,*
> *I'm one of you.*"

"What did you come to do here?"

"To learn and also to teach," said the Rabbi. "Each one of you will do some magic for me."

The witches opened the door. The young men quickly hid themselves outside the cave.

When the Rabbi came into the cave, one of the witches noticed that in spite of the rain he was perfectly dry.

"How is it you're dry when it's raining so hard outside?" she asked in wonder.

"I walked between the raindrops," answered the Rabbi simply.

Satisfied with the answer, the witches began to show their magic. One witch came forward and said:

> "*Mee-lee, mee-lee,*
> *Oak, too, too,*
> *Here's some bread*
> *I've baked for you.*"

Saying these words, she produced a piece of bread. When she had finished her trick, she turned to the Rabbi and asked:

"And you, what can you do?"

Then another witch came up and said:

> "*Boss-nee, boss-nye,*
> *Zubedee,—bye*
> *Here's some meat!*
> *That's nice to fry.*"

And with that, she handed him some meat. When she had finished her stunt, she turned to the Rabbi and asked:

"And you, what can you do?"

Then the third witch said, as she knocked on the floor with a stick:

> "*Goo goo goo*
> *Doo doo doo*
> *This is pudding*
> *For me and for you.*"

Saying that, she brought out some pudding. When she had finished her stunt, she turned to the Rabbi and said:

"And you, what can you do?"

Then a fourth witch, very tall and very lanky, came up. She stretched out her arms and began to move them round and round in a circle, as she said:

> *"Round and round*
> *Curl and wound,*
> *Cocoa, tea, and coffee, too,*
> *Wine the best I bring to you."*

And she handed the Rabbi some wine. When she had finished her stunt, she turned to the Rabbi and said:

"And you, what can you do?"

The Rabbi answered, "I can whistle twice, and so bring eighty men dressed in dry wraps. They will entertain you. And you will surely enjoy them."

So the Rabbi whistled once and the young men put on their wraps, which they had kept dry under the pitchers. Then the Rabbi whistled again and they all rushed into the cave.

Each young man picked up a witch, put her on his camel, and rode away with her.

The witches all married the nice Jewish young men. They became good hard-working women and were the mothers of some great scholars in Israel.

SCHOOL ON THE ROOF

LITTLE by little the Jews began to build schools. These schools were not only for little children, but for big men, with children of their own. I see one of these men, Hillel, at work now.

Whack! Whack! Whack! goes his ax on the wood.

"Hard work, this chopping," says Hillel as he puts down the ax and wipes his face with his handkerchief. "But I have a family to take care of, and I must pay for my schooling, too."

Hillel is grown up but he still keeps on studying. And he works hard to be able to go to school. One-half of what he earns he gives to his family, and the other half he pays the doorkeeper for admission to the school.

Wheez-wheez-z-z, goes the saw on the wood. Hillel begins to saw the wood instead of chopping it. He thinks it might be a little easier.

A few more whacks with the ax and a few more cuts with the saw, and the day is over.

Evening comes and, happily, Hillel goes to the school of Shemayah and Abtalyon. He forgets all about his hard day's work. He forgets all about his family. He forgets that he will have to look for a new job the next day. The whole of Hillel,—his heart and his mind and his body, is listening to the words of the teacher.

But even good things have an end, so school, too, is soon over.

The next morning, Hillel starts out to look for another job. He goes from house to house, but everyone has already prepared enough wood for winter. Hillel is hungry and cold and worried. Where will he get the money to pay the doorkeeper at the school? And what will his family do?

At last the sun is beginning to set. Hillel goes home and eats what little food he can find. Then, as is his habit, he goes to school.

When he comes to the door, the doorkeeper asks him as always, "Where is your dinar?"

"I could not get any work today," mumbles Hillel. "I'll pay you tomorrow."

"Have you a prutah at least?" asks the doorkeeper.

"No. Not even a prutah." Hillel hangs his head.

"Then you can't come in today," says the doorkeeper sternly.

Hillel looks about him. He will find a way. And he does find a way. He will not miss school even for one evening.

Hillel notices that on the top of the roof there is a skylight, and in the skylight a little hole. Quietly Hillel climbs up to the roof and lies down across the skylight, putting his ear to the little hole. From this position he listens to the teachings of the rabbis.

Meanwhile the snow begins to fall. Thicker and still thicker it falls. But Hillel doesn't even notice it. He is too busy listening to the rabbis. And so one of his feet becomes frozen and then the other, and then one arm and then the other arm, until Hillel becomes very weak and faints away.

The next morning when Shemayah and Abtalyon come into the school room, Shemayah says, "Isn't it dark here? And the sun is shining so brightly outside!"

"Yes," answers Abtalyon, "I have been wondering about it." At this moment, they both raise their eyes up to the skylight.

"Why, it looks as if someone is lying up there! Is that possible? It can't be!"

School on the Roof

They hurry up to the roof and there, buried deep in the snow, lies Hillel, all numb.

They take him down and rub him with hot oil until he wakes up. Then Hillel tells them the whole story of how and why he came to the roof. From that day Hillel was admitted without charge to the school.

Some years later Hillel became the head of this very school.

THE BET

HILLEL was so kind and good-natured and, above all, so patient, that even those who were not Jews heard about his good qualities.

One day a heathen said to a Jew:

"I'll bet you four hundred dinar that I can get Hillel angry."

"All right, let's see," said the Jew.

So the heathen found out just when Hillel took his bath, and at that very time he came and cried:

"Hillel! Hillel! Where is Hillel?"

Now this was very disrespectful. Even the rabbis called Hillel, *"Rabbi* Hillel."

Hillel wrapped himself in some coverings and came out.

"What is it, my son? Is there anything I can do for you?" he asked in his quiet, peaceful way.

"Why do the tadmors have sore eyes?"

"Indeed, that is an important question. They have sore eyes because they live near the desert and the sand gets into their eyes and makes them sore." So the heathen went away. And Hillel went back to his bath.

After a few minutes, the heathen returned and again he called:

"Hillel! Hillel! Where is Hillel?"

Again Hillel covered himself and came out.

"Is there anything else I can do for you? I'll be glad to do it," said Hillel kindly.

"Why do the Africans have flat feet?"

"That too is an important question. They have flat feet because they live in the marshes, and, since they walk in flat damp places, their feet get flat, too."

Again the heathen went away.

"I must not lose my four hundred dinar," he muttered to himself. "I'll get Hillel angry yet. I know what I'll do. I'm going to insult him! That will surely make him angry."

So, after a short while, the heathen again came back and again he called:

"Hillel! Hillel! Where is Hillel?"

Again without getting angry, Hillel came out of his bath.

"Is there anything I can tell you, my son? Ask, and I shall be glad to answer."

"Are you the one whom they call Hillel, the Prince of Israel?"

"Yes," said Hillel, "that's what they call me."

"Well, then, I wish there were no others like you in Israel."

"And why do you say that?" asked Hillel, still keeping his temper.

"Because on account of you I shall lose four hundred dinar. I bet four hundred dinar that I could make you angry, and no matter how I tried, I did not succeed."

"Well," smiled Hillel good-naturedly, "it is better that you should lose your money than that Hillel should lose his patience."

TORAH ON ONE FOOT

AT another time the heathens wanted to make fun of the Torah, and of the rabbis. They asked one another:

"Are all rabbis as kind as Hillel? Are all Jewish teachers as good as Hillel? Are all rabbis as patient as Hillel?"

So one of them said:

"I shall go and find out." He came to Shammai, also a famous rabbi, and cried:

"Your Torah, your wonderful Torah—I can learn it while I stand on one foot. Rabbi Shammai, you teach it to me while I stand on one foot." You see, he was just making fun of the Torah.

Now what do you suppose Shammai did? Do you think he had patience with a man who was making fun of the Torah? Who ever heard of learning the whole Torah while standing on one foot? The rabbis had spent all their lives in studying the Torah and even then they were not sure that they knew all of it.

Rabbi Shammai took a stick and shouted angrily:

"Get out of here, you scoffer! Do you think I have

time to waste on people who mock our holy Torah?"

The heathen ran away. He thought he would go to Hillel and see what Hillel would do.

All out of breath, he came to Hillel's home. Hillel thought the man had come for something very important. So Hillel said:

"What is the matter, my good man?" And the heathen answered:

"Teach me the Torah while I stand on one foot."

Of course Hillel, too, saw that the heathen was scoffing, but calmly and patiently he said:

"You want to learn a great deal quickly, don't you? Very well, I shall teach you the Torah while you stand on one foot. This is our Holy Torah: 'What is hateful to you, do not do unto others.'"

The heathen forgot that he had come only to jeer.

"Does it mean that the heathens and the Jews and all of us are brothers? Does it mean that we must be kind to one another like brothers?" asked the heathen, wonderingly.

"That's it, my son. That's the meaning of the whole Torah. All the rest is only an explanation of that. Go, go, my son. Go and study it," said Hillel kindly.

"When may I come for another lesson?" asked the heathen humbly.

TWO WHO WERE WRONG

ONCE there lived in Jerusalem a very rich man. He had a good friend whose name was Kamza. But he also had an enemy who was called Bar Kamza. One day this rich man decided to give a big feast to all his friends. He sent his servant to invite Kamza. But the servant got the names twisted and called "Bar Kamza" instead.

When the great feast day came, all the guests were seated around the long table. It was decked with sparkling dishes of highly polished gold and silver. Great bottles and glasses of all shapes were filled with red and golden wine. Some were placed in the center of the table, and others at each place. Baskets, heavily laden with all kinds of beautiful fruit, stood on the table and in many places around the room.

The rich man entered and saw Bar Kamza among the guests.

"Who invited you?" he shouted to Bar Kamza. "Get out! No one wants you here!"

Bar Kamza's face reddened. He felt ashamed. He called the rich man aside and pleaded:

"Do not disgrace me before all these people. I will pay you for everything I eat and drink if you will let me stay here tonight."

"No. Get out of here."

"I will pay you for half the feast, even half the feast," urged Bar Kamza.

"I don't want you here," answered the rich man, stubbornly.

"I will pay you for the whole feast," cried Bar Kamza, "only don't put me to shame before all these people."

"Nothing you say will make me change my mind," shouted the rich man. "I don't want you, nor your money. Just get out of here," and the rich host pointed to the door.

Bar Kamza could do nothing more. Too ashamed to raise his eyes, he rushed out as quickly as he could.

Do you think Hillel would have done anything so mean? Would Hillel have put anyone to shame? Now there were some rabbis seated at the tables. But they did not object. They allowed the rich man to drive Bar Kamza from his house.

Bar Kamza felt so hurt that he made up his mind to take revenge on his fellow Jews. Just because he, one man, was put to shame, he would hurt all the Jews. That surely was not kind. Bar Kamza, however, could not see that because of his anger. He went to the emperor of Rome and said:

"The Jews have rebelled against you. If you want to prove it send them a calf to sacrifice. You will see that they will refuse to sacrifice it."

Of course, you know, there was a law among the Jews that animals used for sacrificing had to be perfect. They had to be healthy, with every limb whole.

Bar Kamza knew about this law, and so eager was he to avenge himself that when no one was looking, he made a little cut in the upper lip of the calf. The cut was so small that you could hardly notice it; and the animal with the cut lip was taken to the Jews.

"Sacrifice this animal to your God," commanded the king's officers.

As the high priest carefully examined it, he found the cut in its upper lip. Calling some of the elders aside, he said:

"Look, here is a cut in the upper lip."

"Someone must be trying to get us into trouble," said one of the rabbis.

"I wonder who it could be!" exclaimed another.

Presently the rabbi who had spoken at first, said:

"I think I know who it is. This can be no other than Bar Kamza. He was put to shame at the feast and we sat by without a word. What are we to do now?"

"Sacrifice the calf for the sake of peace," replied one of the elders.

"No, no," was heard all over the room. "That's against the law. We won't sacrifice it—peace or no peace!"

So the Jews went to the officers and told them that they could not sacrifice this animal.

"Why, what is the matter with it?" asked the officers.

"You see, its lip is cut, up here. It's against the Jewish law to sacrifice such animals."

"Oh, we know. That is only an excuse. You are all traitors. Don't think you will escape so easily," said the officers as they went away.

"Oh, why didn't we sacrifice that animal?" cried some.

"Why did that rich man put Bar Kamza to shame?" cried others. "Had we been good men, then all this wouldn't have befallen us."

A few weeks later, the emperor of the Romans gathered an army and besieged Jerusalem.

THE SCHOOL THAT SAVED A PEOPLE

I

RABBI Johanan ben Zakkai saw that the end of Jerusalem was near. Every day he walked up and down in his room. His forehead was wrinkled with worry. He was not only worrying; he was thinking very hard.

Finally he exclaimed: "I have it. I know what I shall do!"

Soon you could have seen him hurrying to his pupils at his school. There they were, not children, but men. He found them talking about the siege, and worrying about the lack of food in Jerusalem. As Johanan entered, all became silent.

"I must leave Jerusalem. I must go to see the emperor himself," announced Johanan in a sad voice.

Of course his pupils were eager to know why the rabbi wished to leave the city; but they dared not ask.

The School That Saved a People

Then one plucked up enough courage to say:

"But, Rabbi, you know, that those Jews, who do not want to surrender to the Romans, those Jews who believe we must fight the Romans, they will not——"

"Let anybody either enter or leave the city. They will kill anyone who wants to make peace with the Romans," another pupil ended the sentence.

"We shall find a way. I have something very important to ask of the Emperor. It is the only thing that will save the Jewish people. And they must, they shall be saved!"

There was silence for a while. Everyone was deeply moved. Yet no one had any idea as to what could be done.

"I have a plan. Listen carefully while I tell it to you." The Rabbi did not have to ask this of his pupils. They were only too eager to listen.

"We will spread a rumor," began the Rabbi in a low, clear voice, "that I am sick. And after a few days we will spread another rumor that I am dead."

The eyes of some of the young men lit up. They were beginning to see. Yes, they understood the Rabbi's plan.

"You will get a coffin," continued the Rabbi, "and put me into it. Then you will get permission to bury me."

"Splendid! Fine idea!" cried some.

"But, Rabbi, a dead body always seems much heavier than a living one. Suppose the officers lift the coffin. They will notice that it seems too light," said another pupil slowly and timidly.

The pupils were getting excited. Each one had something to say. They found it hard to listen patiently to one another, as they had always done. Before they knew it, they were all talking together. No one knew what the other was saying.

"Fill the coffin with rags," one voice called loudly above the rest. "Yes, fill it with rags to make it heavier." But even though he screamed he could hardly be heard. Only when the Rabbi began to speak were they all hushed.

"Yes," said the Rabbi, "Joshua made a fine suggestion. We will fill up the coffin, but we must find something heavier than rags."

"Stones will be good," called Eliezer ben Arakh, warmly.

So it was decided that the coffin would be filled with stones and then the pupils would carry it out of the city.

The Rabbi and the pupils went home. Soon the people of Jerusalem, prompted by Johanan's pupils, were saying to one another:

The School That Saved a People

"How sad! Johanan, the great teacher in Israel, is sick, very sick. Johanan, the great rabbi, may die."

A few days later, everybody was mourning for Johanan.

Late at night, when everybody was in bed and even the night-watchmen around the city walls were beginning to get sleepy, the pupils of Rabbi Johanan came to his home all ready to carry the coffin containing the Rabbi and the stones.

It was getting chilly. The Rabbi covered himself with many wraps. The pupils, too, dressed themselves warmly. The Rabbi got into the coffin and it was locked. The students, three at each side and one at each end, carried the coffin. About fourteen walked ahead carrying lanterns to light the way, and so they passed through the city. Not a person could be seen or heard. Not even a dog barked. Neither the moon nor the stars were out.

Can you see them as they walked along? They were hopeful, yet a little afraid.

"How will it all turn out?" they wondered. They stopped once to relieve those who were carrying the coffin.

Suddenly they heard an officer calling to them. Trembling, they stopped. Those who were holding the coffin could hardly keep from dropping it.

The School That Saved a People

"What are you doing out here, so late?" asked the officer sternly.

"Rabbi Johanan died and we are carrying his body out of the city to be buried," answered Joshua, whom they had chosen as their spokesman. The officer hardly listened to their answer, commanding them to pass on.

And on they continued in silence. They were just aching to speak to the Rabbi. They were just aching to find out how he was feeling and to tell him that all was well. They did not know whether he could hear everything or not. But on they had to walk in silence. They dared not take any chances. Suppose someone should come along and hear them talk into the coffin. No. They had to hurry out of the city as quickly as possible.

Ben Biatach, one of the Jews who believed that they must fight the Romans, was a friend of Rabbi Johanan. So, when the pupils had at last reached the city walls they had no trouble there.

Soon they found themselves outside the city walls. There were the Roman soldiers, drinking and singing. Some could hardly stand on their feet from drunkenness. But they still knew what they were there for. As the lanterns and the coffin approached them, one of the soldiers staggered over and said:

"Don't you know the law?"

"Yes, but all we want is to bury our Rabbi."

On hearing this, a few of the officers came over to the coffin. The students could hear their hearts thump. What would the officers do?

Sure enough, they lifted up the coffin and found it quite heavy.

"Heavy man, your Rabbi," one laughed.

"From this it does not seem that they are starving yet in Jerusalem," jeered another.

The students remained quiet all this time.

Then one of the soldiers took out his spear and motioning to them to open the coffin, he said, "I'll just stab once to make sure he is dead."

This was altogether unexpected. Beads of cold sweat stood out on the students' foreheads. What should they do? What should they say?

Then Joshua walked over and made as if he were going to unlock the coffin. But he stopped and in a tearful voice begged the soldiers:

"Please, please don't dishonor, don't defile the body of our Rabbi. Among us Jews it is a great insult to stab a body. You know only too well, that our Rabbi is dead."

"Aw, let them pass. They have wasted too much of our time as it is. Come, come let us go back. Let

The School That Saved a People

us drink a little more for the night will soon be over." Saying this, they threw their arms across one another's shoulders and walked away.

The students could hear the soldiers singing as they went on their way:

*"Hey-ho-hey-ho,
Then fill another cup,—
Hey-ho-hey-ho."*

They smiled to each other and began to sing along with the soldiers: "Hey-ho-hey-ho——."

They were so very happy. In a few minutes, they would be a safe distance from the walls. Then they would open the coffin and all their fears would be over.

At last—it seemed like years to them—they set down the coffin. Breathlessly they opened it. Then they heaved one long sigh-h-h-h—as the Rabbi greeted them with a smile.

They did not wait to be thanked, but wishing Rabbi Johanan success, returned home.

The Jerusalem sky was ablaze with many, many colors. A new day was dawning. What would it bring?

II

Now what was Rabbi Johanan's wish? Was it really so important? Think of it, the Rabbi had risked his life for it! His pupils had helped him most willingly, but they had no idea why the Rabbi had gone to the general, Vespasian.

It was afternoon when Rabbi Johanan appeared before Vespasian, the general. Vespasian had heard of Rabbi Johanan. He knew that the Rabbi had always desired peace with the Romans. So he felt kindly towards Johanan.

"Blessed be the Emperor Vespasian," said Rabbi Johanan as he came in.

"For that, you ought to die twice," Vespasian answered angrily. "First of all, I am not an emperor; so you are just making fun of me. Secondly, if I am the Emperor, why haven't you come to me before this?"

"I didn't come to you sooner because they would not let me out of the city. And I tell you again you are, you are the Emperor."

Just as Rabbi Johanan was saying these words, a messenger from Rome was ushered in.

"Hail to the Emperor Vespasian!" saluted the messenger. "The Emperor has just died and you have been made the new Emperor."

Vespasian was of course very happy. He liked Rabbi Johanan even better than ever.

"Is there anything I can do for you?" he asked.

The School That Saved a People

"Yes, I came to ask a little favor," answered the Rabbi. "Sooner or later the Romans will capture Jerusalem. Now all I ask is that you allow me to build a Jewish School in Javneh. That is a little town not far from Jerusalem."

"Your wish will surely be granted," said Vespasian. To himself he thought, "That Rabbi is foolish, after all. He could have asked for a high position in the kingdom, or for some expensive jewels—something worth while, something big, something important. Instead he asked for such a trifle."

Rabbi Johanan, however, was very happy. He had staked his life. He might have been killed in the coffin but he had succeeded in the end. Perhaps Jerusalem would be destroyed. Jews would be killed or driven out of Jerusalem. Perhaps they would be driven all over the world. But they would not die out. They would have the school in Javneh. That school would teach the Jewish children and the Jewish young men and women. That school at Javneh would tell them of the sad and the happy days of the Jews. That school would tell them of the wonderful, wonderful heroes of the Jews. That school would keep the Jewish people together. That school would keep the Jewish people alive. Johanan journeyed to Javneh immediately and began to build that most important school.

ENOUGH FOR WASH DAY

HUNDREDS and hundreds of Roman soldiers guarded the walls of Jerusalem so that no one might go in or come out of the city.

What do you think would happen to the people of Jerusalem? Their food couldn't last forever. Neither could their water, for they had no running water as most people now have. Before long they had nothing to eat and nothing to drink.

That was just what the Romans were waiting for. There were no battles. They just wanted to keep the Jews in the city until they would either starve or give themselves up to the Romans. They would have to surrender.

One day the Roman soldiers noticed some wet sheets and blankets hanging over the walls.

"Those Jews must have lots of water," said one soldier to another.

"If they knew what was good for them they would save their water for drinking. What a waste! Poor fools. Don't they know it is better to keep alive than to have clean sheets for a day!"

But what do you think was really going on in the Jewish camp? I wonder if you can guess? Do you think that the Jews really had enough water to bathe in? Do you think they had enough water to wash their clothes?

No. Of course not! They were just reaching the end of their supply. But would they let the Romans know it? They would rather die! So what did they do? They let their throats get dry and dipped their sheets into the little water they had left! "Let the Romans think we have plenty!" they said. Can you imagine anyone washing towels when he has not enough water to drink?

Can you imagine such bravery?

THE TEMPLE IN RUINS

When Johanan returned to Jerusalem a few weeks after his remarkable escape from the city, he found the Jews still holding out bravely against the Romans. As he came close to the walls of the city, he heard these cries:

"Pour it down."

"First see whether it is hot enough."

"No, throw down the stones."

With their last bit of strength, the Jews were pouring oil, throwing stones and everything else they could lay hold of, over the walls.

But they could not hold out much longer. Men, women and children were dying of hunger. The bodies of the dead were strewn all over the ground. Imagine the Jews living amidst these stuffy odors. You surely remember the story of the suffering at the destruction of the first Temple. But this was worse.

The Temple in Ruins

The high priest, to whom the keys of the Temple were entrusted, clasped them tightly and would let no one go near the Temple. But, alas! He could not stop the Romans! They broke through the walls. They set the Temple on fire. This was a terrible thing for the high priest to behold, but still he held the keys. When, right before his eyes he saw the Temple fall, his courage left him. What was the use of holding on to the keys now! So first he threw the keys into the flames—and then leaped in himself.

Nor was he the only one. Many others threw themselves into the flames after him. Still others fell on their own swords. How could they live on if the Temple was gone?

The Roman soldiers began to shout:
"Down with the Temple!"
"Down with Jerusalem."
"Hail, hail! All victory to the Romans!"
While from the Jews came:
"Woe, woe. The Temple has fallen!" "Jerusalem is destroyed!"

Sssss-S-S. Tz-tz-tz-tz. Came the fierce hissing of the flames. Jerusalem destroyed! Jerusalem no more!

"Oh woe, oh woe!" shrieked the onlookers.

Sad at heart, Johanan stood by while all this was going on. But hopefully he exclaimed:

"No, no! We shall not die. We shall live on. Yes, the school at Jamnia, the little school at Jamnia will keep us alive."

Thus the second Temple was destroyed. Jerusalem was plundered. The Jews were scattered all over the world. But they lived on!

ABC AT TWENTY-TWO

"Rocks, rocks, and again rocks," said Eliezer ben Hyrcanus to himself. "It certainly is very hard to plow here. Besides, I don't like to plow; I don't want to plow. I don't want to plow here or anywhere else, even if the ground were smooth and level. Oh, I do wish father would let me go away to study!" Eliezer put his plow aside, sat down on one of the rocks and began to cry. Just then his father, who had been observing him, came over to him.

"What!" he called, "You, a man of twenty-two crying. What's the matter? Is anything wrong with you? Oh, maybe you are tired of plowing among the rocks. Well, there are enough fields. You can change off with your brothers who are plowing in the smooth, level fields."

But Eliezer didn't seem to hear his father at all. He sat and cried just as before.

"Why don't you answer me?" demanded his father sternly.

"Oh, I don't want to plow all my life; I want to go to school and study all about my people. Why haven't you ever sent me to school?"

"What!—You, a man of twenty-two, wish to begin to go to school? Ha, ha, ha! You make me laugh. You ought to be married and taking your children to school."

"Well, I wanted to tell you for some time, father," Eliezer said. "I've made up my mind; I'm going to study."

"You won't do anything of the kind," answered Hyrcanus. "You won't get anything to eat until this whole field is plowed."

So Eliezer got up very, very early and plowed the whole field. As he was finishing his plowing, he fell and broke his leg.

Through all his pain, Eliezer thought, "At any rate, this will give me a good excuse for going away to study until my leg gets well." And so it turned out. Eliezer went to Javneh to the school which Johanan ben Zakkai had built.

Eliezer supported by a crutch, hopped along very slowly from six o'clock one day, until six o'clock the next day.

At last, hungry and tired, he came to Johanan. Approaching Johanan he said:

"I am twenty-two years old, but I have never gone to school. Please teach me the blessings, and some Hebrew. Maybe later on I shall be able to study Torah." So Johanan began to teach Eliezer.

All this time Eliezer had scarcely anything to eat. He began to look very pale. He could hardly speak. In fact, he could hardly stand. Rabbi Johanan noticed this. One morning he asked Eliezer kindly:

"Have you had your breakfast yet, my son?" Eliezer did not reply.

Rabbi Johanan repeated, "Eliezer, have you had your breakfast yet?"

"Oh!" answered Eliezer, as if he had not heard the Rabbi before, "I have eaten at the house where I stay."

Rabbi Johanan knew that Eliezer was not telling the truth. And so he sent a number of his pupils to Eliezer's lodging place to find out what they could about Eliezer's meals. There the housekeeper told them that Eliezer had never eaten at her house. "But," she said, "he has a sack, and often I see him put his head into it and suck something. It looks as if he were sucking from a bottle." Having heard her story, they went up to his room and found the sack. When they opened it, they found it full of earth. The pupils returned to the Rabbi and told him the story. Rabbi Johanan then invited Eliezer to eat with him.

For three years he lived and studied with Rabbi Johanan. But all these years Eliezer did not write any letters to his father, because there was no way of getting them delivered. And Eliezer was too weak to walk such a great distance.

At last Eliezer's brothers said:

"How long will you wait for Eliezer to return? He does not care for you. He is waiting until you die. Then he will come and claim his share of your riches. Go up to Jerusalem and make a will saying that Eliezer shall not receive any of your land or money."

Hyrcanus thought a while. Then he said:

"I guess you are right. He is no son of mine. He never told me why or where he was going. He does not care whether I live or die. So—why should I care about him? Tomorrow I shall leave for Javneh."

When Hyrcanus came to Javneh, Rabbi Johanan was holding a feast. The rich and learned men of the city had been invited. Johanan, hearing that Hyrcanus was in town, invited him, too. Everything was ready. All sat down to the feast.

Then Rabbi Johanan called on Eliezer to explain certain parts of the Torah.

Eliezer blushed. He felt nervous to think that he, Eliezer, should explain things before all these learned men!

"No, Rabbi, please. I can't—not before all these men."

"Don't be foolish, Eliezer," said Rabbi Johanan. "You can do it as well as anybody else."

Eliezer's face lit up. His eyes began to sparkle. The room seemed lit up as if by sun rays. In a clear, loud voice he began to recite the Torah. When he finished, Rabbi Johanan arose and kissed him. "Blessed are Abraham, Isaac and Jacob that you are a great, great grandson of theirs."

When Hyrcanus heard this, he could no longer keep quiet.

"No, no," he called, "blessed am I, who have such a learned son. My son, Eliezer—a rabbi in Israel." Then Hyrcanus mounted the platform. "Listen, O men of Jamnia," said Hyrcanus through his tears. "I came to Jerusalem to tell the people that Eliezer would no longer be a son of mine. His brothers told me not to give him his share of my riches. And I was about to do as they had suggested. But instead he shall be my only heir. To Eliezer, to him who starved himself to become a learned man—to him I will give all my fortune."

A B C at Twenty-two

Thus, though Eliezer had been very poor as a student, he became a very rich and famous rabbi—Rabbi Eliezer ben Hyrcanus.

But as you may have expected, Eliezer did not keep the whole fortune for himself. Even though his brothers had been so unjust to him, he divided his fortune with them.

THE WICKED NEIGHBOR

Most of the rabbis were very poor. But the poorest of all was Haninah ben Dosah. Even on Friday, his wife had nothing to cook and nothing to bake. You know how busy your mother is on Friday. You know what good odors come out of the kitchen. You can smell the freshly baked pies, cakes, and cookies. You can smell the chicken soup. But the wife of Ben Dosah didn't even have to build the fire, for she had nothing to cook on it.

"Dear me!" she said. "All the women around me are busy getting ready for Shabbas. Only my home is cold and empty. I don't want them to pity us. Who can tell? Some kind neighbor may even bring us some food. O dear! O dear! What shall I do?"

You know at that time they did not have gas ranges or even coal stoves. They had ovens made of earthen clay. So Ben Dosah's wife took some wood and built a fire. The wood burned and the smoke went up through the chimney.

It didn't take long before all the neighbors were talking about the wonderful thing that had happened. Haninah's wife had something to cook and to bake. And most of them were happy.

Now Ben Dosah's wife had one wicked neighbor. When she saw the smoke coming out of the chimney, she thought:

"The Rabbi's wife has nothing in her oven. What is all that smoke about? I must go in to see what she is burning in her oven." So the wicked neighbor threw her shawl over her shoulders and walked across to the Rabbi's house. She knocked at the door and waited a while. The Rabbi's wife, however, was ashamed to meet her. Therefore, instead of answering the knock, she ran into the next room. Again the wicked neighbor knocked at the door.

"O dear!" she thought. "I guess she is ashamed to meet me. Well, I'll go in anyway." So without waiting for any answer to her knock, she quickly opened the door and went into the house.

What do you think she saw? There on the stove all kinds of puddings and Shabbas dishes were being prepared. And she could smell cherry pies and honey cookies in the stove. It even seemed to her that she smelled the cookies burning.

When she saw all this she called to the Rabbi's

wife, "Hurry up, bring in your cookie turner. Your cookies are burning."

"What was that? What did you say?" the Rabbi's wife called from the other room. She was sure that she hadn't heard aright, because she knew that there was nothing in the stove. "Is it possible that she is making fun of me?" the Rabbi's wife thought as she was about to grasp her long cookie turner.

"Well, what are you waiting for? Hurry before they are all burnt," the neighbor's voice was heard again.

The Rabbi's wife, full of joy, seized her cookie turner and ran into the kitchen. She was blushing. But it didn't matter. She looked as if she were hot because of the hard work. Going over to the stove, she touched the cookies to make sure that they were real, and said:

"I had just run out to get my cookie turner when you knocked on the door."

Now it was the wicked neighbor who felt ashamed, and without another word she went home.

THE SHEPHERD RABBI

"It's so cool here. Let us sit down and rest," said Akiba, a tall, dark youth. He and Rachel, the daughter of the rich landowner, Kalba Seabua, were walking along the banks of a brook. They were very happy together. Everything seemed beautiful to them.

Rachel, too, wanted to sit down. So they did.

Ah-h-h-h, Akiba heaved a big sigh.

"Why have you become so sad? Only a minute ago you seemed so gay," said Rachel in her sweet, soft voice.

"How can I be happy when I know that I shall never be able to marry you? I am only a poor shepherd. But you are beautiful and a rich man's daughter."

"But you are not an ordinary shepherd," said Rachel angrily.

"You think so because you love me." Akiba smiled a sweet, sad smile.

"Well, I do love you, and I am going to marry you. You will go to school and become a rabbi in Israel." Akiba thought he hadn't heard aright.

"What did you say?" he asked, sure that he had been dreaming.

The sun was setting. How suddenly it had grown dark! Why, they had sat there but a few minutes, thought Akiba and Rachel. Surprised at the hour, they both quickly got up and parted.

With flushed cheeks and sparkling eyes, Rachel danced into her big, beautiful, rich home singing:

"Akiba, Akiba, a shepherd is he.
Akiba, Akiba, a rabbi shall be!"

Rachel's father looked at her closely as she came in.

"Again you have been in the company of that poor, dirty, ignorant shepherd—that shepherd who knows nothing!"

"Yes, I have," said Rachel calmly. "And I'm going to marry that poor, dirty, ignorant shepherd. And I will help him become a great rabbi in Israel."

"Then you shall leave this house and never return to it again." And that was exactly what Rachel did.

Akiba and Rachel were married. They were very,

very poor. They slept on a bed of straw. And they had nothing but bread to eat and water to drink. They lived this way for some time and were very, very happy. But what were they to do? They couldn't live on bread and water forever.

Rachel, however, was not only beautiful; she was also very clever and sensible. So she said to Akiba:

"You go to Javneh and study there at Rabbi Johanan's school. And I will wait. Meanwhile I shall live as best I can. Then, when you will have become a great rabbi in Israel, you will come back and we shall be together again."

Akiba felt both happy and sad. He loved Rachel and did not want to part from her. But he loved the Torah, too, and he wanted to become a scholar. So, after a few days, with a heavy heart, Akiba left his beloved wife to study under the great Rabbi Johanan.

Do you know of any woman who made such a sacrifice? Think of it! Rachel had no automobiles, no maids—why, she didn't even have a dining room! Her living room, her bedroom, and her kitchen, all were one little hut. But how she loved Akiba! How she wanted him to become a great man! Therefore she did not mind giving up her comforts.

Many people said to her:

"Foolish girl, for whom are you waiting? Do you

think Akiba will ever come back to you? Do you suppose he still remembers you? Go—get married to a good man!"

"No—no," she would answer. "You don't know my Akiba. He will stay away until he becomes a rabbi in Israel and then he will come back."

Rachel did not see her beloved Akiba for twelve years, while he was studying hard at the school. For twelve long years, she lived all alone in a poor little hut. Wasn't she a great heroine?

In the meantime, Akiba entered the school at Jamnia as a poor student. After a few years, he became the head of that same school. He was greatly respected and honored by everybody. At last he was ready to return to his home, to his beloved Rachel.

Would she recognize him, he wondered. Would he recognize her? Was she still as beautiful as when he had left her?

At last, the news came that the great Rabbi Akiba was coming to the little town. All the important people in the town were busy. All were excited. Each wanted his house to look the finest. Each wanted the Rabbi to be his guest. No one knew, and no one dreamed that there was one heart that beat faster than any of theirs,—that there was one soul that was happier than even the happiest among them.

The Shepherd Rabbi

At last the news spread through the town that the great Rabbi Akiba was approaching. He was already in town. Young and old, man, woman and child, all came forth to greet him.

Rachel, in her poor, shabby garments, stood silently by. When she saw Akiba, she gave a little start, just a very little move to approach him. But some of Akiba's students pushed her aside.

"Woman," they said gruffly, "where are you trying to go? Don't you know this is the great Rabbi Akiba?"

Rachel blushed and hung her head. In the meantime, Akiba had already seen her. Though she was no longer so beautiful, Akiba knew that it was still his own dear Rachel who stood before him. Making his way through the crowd of students, he said:

"Let that woman come up here." Then, changing his mind, "Nay—I will go up to her. If I *am* a great man it is all due to her. Had she not given up everything, I could never have become what I am. Had she not had so much patience, I could never have reached this great position." Saying these words, he embraced Rachel and kissed her.

Meanwhile a message had come from one of the rich men of the city asking Rabbi Akiba to come to his house. Akiba explained to Rachel that he must leave her for a little while before he could come to their hut. As always, Rachel understood, and Akiba hurried to the rich man.

When Akiba arrived, the rich man said:

"I want to talk to you about something which has been troubling me for twelve years. You are a wise rabbi. Perhaps you will be able to help me." Akiba modestly remained silent. The rich man continued, "Twelve years ago, my daughter married an ignorant, stupid beggar. At that time I took an oath that I would never, never see her again. Now I am getting old. I may die very soon. And I do want to see my daughter, my only child. Perhaps I shall be able to help her a little, just a little, to make up for all the sorrow I have caused her." By this time, the old man had begun to cry.

"Is there a way of doing that, without breaking my oath?"

"Had your daughter married a rabbi, would you have taken that oath?" asked Rabbi Akiba.

"Ha, ha, a rabbi—if that shepherd had only been able to read the prayers I should have been satisfied. Alas, she did not marry a rabbi. She married a stupid beggar."

"Well," answered Akiba slowly, "I don't know whether I'm a famous rabbi, but I surely *am* Akiba, the shepherd whom your daughter Rachel married."

On hearing this, Rachel's father fell at the feet of the great rabbi and begged for forgiveness.

Akiba raised him up at once and said: "Do not be troubled about the past. We all make mistakes." They both hurried to Rachel's hut and told her the story.

So, on that day, Rachel was rewarded for her patience and hard work. Not only had she regained the love and riches of her father, but her husband, now a great rabbi, had also come back to her. And so they all lived happily ever after.

THE COCK, THE DONKEY, AND THE CANDLE

Cock-a-doodle-doo.
Cock-a-doodle-doo.

DID you hear that cock crow? That was Akiba's cock. Do you wonder why Akiba carried a cock with him wherever he went? Well, Akiba had no clock, and surely no alarm clock. So whenever the cock crowed, Akiba knew it was time to wake up. He knew that the morning had come.

Cock-a-doodle-doo.
Cock-a-doodle-doo.
Get up, get up, Akiba,
It's studying time for you.

"It's hard work studying to be a rabbi, but how fine it is to be a wise and learned man," thought Akiba as he got up quickly.

He mounted his donkey, which like the cock, accompanied him on his travels. For you remember, of

The Cock, the Donkey, and the Candle

course, that Akiba had no automobile, no train and not even a horse on which to ride.

All day he traveled through hot, sandy places. At last, night came. Akiba, tired, hungry, and thirsty, came into a little town. Bashfully, he walked over to a house. Quietly he knocked on the door. He waited a while. There was no answer. Again he knocked. This time a cross old lady opened the door just far enough to stick her head out and say, "What beggar is knocking now? Get you gone, you tramp." And bang! went the door. Akiba was left outside, hungrier and thirstier than ever.

"Never mind," said Akiba to himself, "whatever God does, he does for the best. Poor woman, she ought to be pitied for being so mean."

Slowly he led his donkey to the next house. Without knocking, he pleaded quietly:

"Please, please let me in. I'm not a beggar; I'm only a poor traveler. Give me a drink of water and some bread. I will pay you for it."

This time a gruff young man opened the door and growled, "Oh, we know your kind. Leave this door, you drunkard, before I throw you into the street."

Without saying a word, Akiba quietly walked away, and thought, "Whatever God does, he does for the best."

The Cock, the Donkey, and the Candle

"Well—I'll try once more," he said good-naturedly. "But this is a pretty bad town. Or else, maybe I do look like a dirty tramp now." Akiba slowly dragged himself over to another door. Again he knocked lightly.

"Please open your door for a poor traveler," said Akiba. After what seemed a long time, an old man opened the door, looked at Akiba once, twice and three times.

"Will you let," Akiba began, but before he could finish his sentence, the man slammed the door in his face. "That must be all right, too," he thought, "for whatever God does, he does for the best."

Wearily, since there was no place where he might rest, Akiba mounted his donkey again, and a little discouraged, he rode toward the woods.

On the way, he found a spring. He drank one cup of water, then another and another. It seemed as though he would drink the spring dry. Then he found a stale piece of bread in his bag. So Akiba made the best of what he had.

In the midst of the woods, he came upon an open space. There he halted his donkey and let the cock roost above him. He then spread a mat on the ground, lit a candle, opened one of his books and began to study.

Suddenly he heard his donkey bray, "Hee, hee, hee." Then there was a lot of noise and uproar. Quickly Akiba ran over. There was a big lion killing the donkey. "Poor animal," Akiba thought. He was so sorry he could do nothing to help. How would he ever reach the school on foot? The donkey had walked slowly enough. But now it would be still worse, thought Rabbi Akiba.

But he wasn't upset; he didn't become excited. He simply said, "Whatever the Lord does, he does for the best." Again he sat down, and opened his book to study.

He had hardly finished a sentence, when again he heard a terrific noise. As Akiba looked up, the cock fell at his feet. "Poor cock," said Akiba. "But whatever God does, he does for the best." And once more Akiba sat down and tried to study a little before going to sleep. When, whew-whew, along came a strong wind and blew out the candle.

Wouldn't that have made you angry? But not so Akiba. He just lit the candle again, and sat down to study. But the wind blew so hard it was not possible to keep the candle lit. So Akiba gave up and went to sleep, saying, "Whatever God does, he does for the best."

Akiba slept through the night and got up quite late

the next morning. You see the cock was not there to wake him.

"Now Akiba took his little bundle of books and returned to the town where he had been treated so unkindly the night before. To his great surprise the people whom he had seen only the night before were dead.

At last he found a little boy weeping. "What has happened in this town, my little son?" Akiba asked.

"Last—n-night," sobbed the little boy,—"robbers came and killed all these people."

"Don't cry," said Akiba kindly, "come with me and I will help you find your relatives in the next town." Then Akiba thought:

"So it was all for the best that I was not allowed to enter their homes.

"It was all for the best, too, that the donkey and the cock had been killed. It was all for the best that the wind blew out the candle.

"Had the donkey brayed, had the cock crowed, had the candle burned, then the robbers would have found me. I, too, would have been killed and I should never have become a rabbi.

"I see more clearly than ever, whatever God does, he does for the best." And Akiba continued on his journey.

FISH OUT OF WATER

DAY after day, Akiba studied the Torah. Day after day, many pupils came to listen to the great Rabbi Akiba. Akiba's school soon became a large public assembly.

Meanwhile, the Romans were becoming more and more cruel to the Jews. Jerusalem had been taken from them and most of the other cities, too. And still the little nation of Jews was alive. The Romans began to understand now. It was the schools that kept the Jews alive.

So one day the Roman king ordered that all Jewish schools be closed and no one be allowed to study the Torah. When this order was sent out, what do you suppose Akiba did? Did he give up his studies? Not at all. He kept on studying and working just as hard as ever. It seemed as if Akiba had never heard of the Roman law. His friends became greatly worried about

Fish Out of Water

him. They feared the Romans would kill him; so they said to him:

"Akiba, please, for the sake of your wife and your friends, please stop studying the Torah." But Akiba listened to no one.

At this time there lived a very wise man called Pappus. One day he came to Akiba and spoke to him about the Romans. He asked him:

"Aren't you afraid of the government? Before long you will surely be killed!"

Then Akiba became impatient and said: "Listen, Pappus, and I will tell you a story——

"Once a fox came over to a pond. He saw the fish throwing themselves hither and thither. There was great noise and excitement. So the fox said to the fish:

> *'Big fish and little fish*
> *In the water splashing,*
> *Big fish and little fish,*
> *Whither are you dashing?'*

Answered the Fish:

> *'O big fox, O wise fox,*
> *The fisherman has his net,*
> *O great fox, O wise fox,*

Fish Out of Water

*Woe to the fish
The fisherman met.'*

*'Ha, ha, ha,' the fox laughed loud,
'Ha, ha, ha,' the fox laughed long,
'Come out, O fish, on dry land you'll be strong.
Come out, O fish, on dry land you belong.'*

" *'Chee, chee, chee,'* now it was the fish who did the laughing.

" *'Is that you speaking? We have heard so much about your wisdom. But now we see that you are only a stupid animal. Just think of it! Here in the water, where we are at home, and where we can live, we are afraid. How much more uncomfortable will we be on dry land! Uncomfortable! Why, then we shall surely die!'* " When Akiba finished his story he looked closely at Pappus.

"Do you understand that?" he finally asked Pappus. "You speak to me just as the fox spoke to the fish. You say to me and to the Jewish people, 'Don't stay in the water, that is, don't study the Torah. Come out on dry land, that is, stop teaching the Torah and kill yourself.'

"Don't you see, Pappus, that Torah is my whole life? If I give up the Torah I can't live. Without Torah I may as well be dead, just like the fish on dry land.

"You see, Pappus, you say to me, 'Akiba, don't wait until you are killed. Stop studying the Torah.' That is as if you would say, 'Don't wait to be killed—but just go and kill yourself.'"

When Akiba had finished explaining the story, Pappus was ashamed and walked away.

But soon thereafter, Akiba and nine other rabbis were killed because they studied and taught Torah.

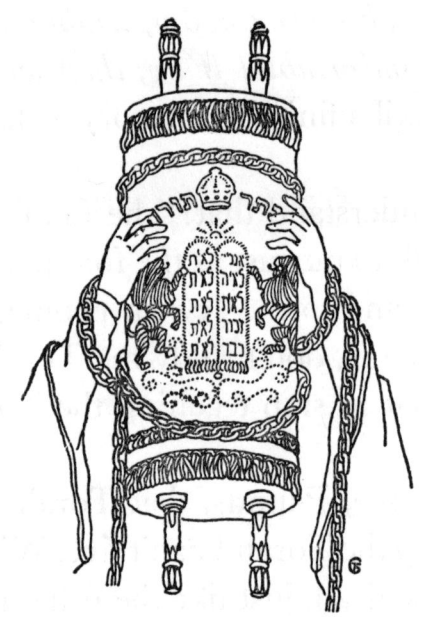

THE GUARDIANS OF THE TORAH

RABBI MEIR was very, very bright. So bright was he, that they called him "Light." (You know "Meir" in Hebrew means "giver of light.") Meir made everything clear to his big pupils, and he made his little pupils bright and happy. Meir liked little children even more than any of the other rabbis did. One day, when a strong wind was blowing outside, many children came into the large synagogue. Rabbi Meir sat down and they formed a circle about him. They stopped all their talking. They didn't even whisper. "Oh, why doesn't he begin?" they wondered. "And why does Rabbi Meir look so sad?"

"Children," said Rabbi Meir at last, "today I shall not tell you a funny story. The story I shall tell you is not sad either, but it's hard to understand. So listen very carefully.

"Once upon a time—long, long ago—God wanted to give the Torah to us Jews. 'But,' the Lord said, 'they will have to give me something very dear to them. If they don't live up to the laws of the Torah, then I shall not return that which they have given me.' So all the Jewish people gathered around Mount Sinai and the Lord called out:

" 'Here is the Torah. I will give it to you—if you give me good security.

"There was a general bustle among the people. One man said, 'Let us give a large sum of money.' Another said, 'No, let us give all our jewelry.' Still another said, 'Let us give our very finest silks and velvets.'

" 'You speak foolishly,' said a third man. 'All of these things are nothing. Today they are won, tomorrow they are gone. Let us offer the stars. If we break this Law—this Torah, then may the stars never shine for us again.'

" 'That's too much to give,' said a younger man. 'Think of it, what will this world be without the beautiful, shining, twinkling stars in the sky?'

" 'Oh, you foolish young man,' said several people at once. 'We shall hold the Torah dear and the stars will always shine for us.'

"At last they all turned to the Lord and called:

> 'Neither money nor jewels
> Do we offer thee,
> But the stars, the twinkling stars
> Our security shall be.'

"'I cannot accept them, O Israel,' said the Lord. 'These are not lasting. Perhaps the stars will not shine forever.'

"Again the people all spoke at once,

"'Let us give the moon,' said they. 'We shall have to be very careful indeed. Think what it would mean if we did not have the beautiful moon at night.' So they said to the Lord:

> 'Neither money nor stars
> Do we offer thee,
> But the moon, the beautiful moon
> Our security shall be.'

"'I cannot accept that,' said the Lord. 'That too may not last forever.'

"'Let us give the sun. That surely will be accepted.'

"So they shouted:

> 'Neither gold nor silver
> Do we offer thee.

The Guardians of the Torah

*The sun, the gleaming sun
Our security shall be.'*

" 'No, I cannot accept even that. The sun, too, may not last forever,' said the Lord.

"Now all became silent. Neither money, nor jewels, nor the stars, nor the moon, nor the sun was accepted. Everybody was puzzled. No one could think of anything more costly, more valuable than what had been offered. A deep silence reigned. It seemed as if the Jews would have to do without the Torah.

"The Lord was about to take the Torah away when a woman cried:

" 'Lord, O Lord. Wait—please wait. I know what we will give—our children. Yes, our children—our very children we shall offer.'

"All were waiting breathlessly. Would the Lord accept the children? Would he consider them good guardians of the Torah? As they were wondering, they heard the Lord say:

" 'Yes, your children shall be the guardians of the Torah. Here it is. Take it, but your children shall guard it.' And so the Torah was given to the Jews."

Rabbi Meir stopped speaking. Not a sound could be heard. There was no clapping of hands. No one even stirred.

After a long silence, one little boy asked:

"Rabbi Meir, does it mean that we children sitting here must be good Jews, or else the Torah will be taken from us?"

"That's right, Simeon, that's exactly it," answered the Rabbi. "You sitting here, and your children after you—and your children's children after them—and so on forever and ever. Do you see how important you are, and all children after you?"

The children looked very happy. They liked this story even more than the funny ones. They felt grown up and responsible.

"If it depends on us," they said, "then we know that the Jews will never, never have to give back the Torah."

KI-TOV—'TWAS GOOD

"Today, I will tell you about Ki-Tov or 'Twas Good," Rabbi Meir said, as the children were gathering round him.

"Some time ago I stopped at a little inn in a country town. At night I heard the innkeeper call:

" 'Get up, get up. Whoever will come now, I will take on my donkeys!' Most of the guests were very happy. It would spare them so much trouble. And think of all the time they would save. So I could hear them answer sleepily,

" 'Wait, I'll hurry——'

" 'Wait, wait, I'm coming,' and quickly they got into their clothes.

"Now I thought it was strange for the innkeeper who was not known as a generous man, to be so kind to his guests. Why should he take all of them on his donkeys? Of course I could not be certain, but I knew that the innkeeper was not kind enough to do so much for his guests. I wanted to warn them not to go, but before I knew it they were all gone. Afterwards I learnt that the innkeeper had arranged with a band of robbers to wait for him in the thick of the woods. When the innkeeper's guests arrived, they were robbed and killed.

"So when the innkeeper called again, I said:

" 'No, thank you, I appreciate your kindness, but I cannot go.'

" 'Why not,' urged the innkeeper, 'tomorrow you will have to travel all that way on foot.'

" 'I know, but I must wait for my brother.'

" 'Where is he? Maybe I can get him for you now. What's his name?' anxiously asked the innkeeper.

" 'Oh, he must be in some synagogue now, where the men are busy studying Torah. His name is Ki-Tov or 'Twas Good.'

"The innkeeper went away and searched in every synagogue. He called, 'Ki-Tov, Ki-Tov, 'Twas Good, 'Twas Good, your brother is waiting for you at my inn. Come out, come out, from wherever you are!' But all in vain. Ki-Tov did not answer.

"After his other guests had been robbed and killed, the innkeeper came home. By that time the sun

had risen and I was not afraid to start on my journey. I packed up and said good-bye to the innkeeper.

" 'Oh, you are going without your brother! I thought you were waiting for your brother Ki-Tov, last night.'

" 'That's true. I didn't lie to you. My brother has already arrived.'

" 'Where is he?' asked the innkeeper as he looked about him puzzled.'

" 'Look up to the sky—do you see that big light-shedding sun? That's my brother, 'Twas Good or Ki-Tov. You see why I call him Ki-Tov or 'Twas Good? Because when God made the sun, he looked at it and said, "Ki-Tov—for 'Twas Good." '

" 'So good-bye, dear Sir. I'm off with my brother, 'Twas Good.' "

The children all clapped their hands and laughed heartily.

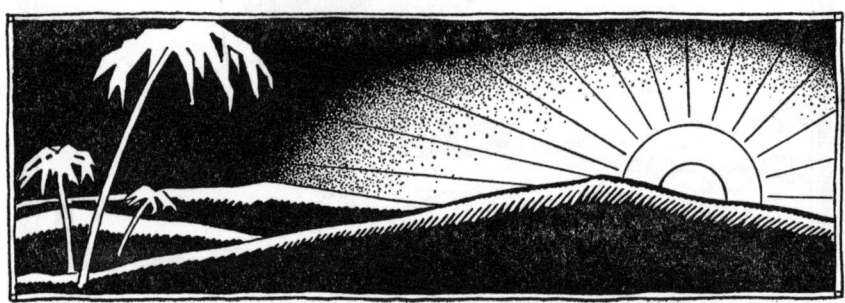

AS FAITHFUL AS THAT

*"Who knows one,
Who knows one?
One is Allah;
One is Allah—"*

Do YOU hear that nasal, sing-song tune? Do you see that man wrapped in a brown abaye (gown)? And do you see his tan turban wound round his head?

That man is an Arab of long ago. He is praying in one of those temples with round domes above them. Those temples are the Arabic temples called mosques.

*"Who knows one,
Who knows one?
One is Allah;
One is Allah."*

His voice rings out through the silent air.

The Jews had scattered throughout the world, and were now in a country called Arabia.

Amongst the Arabian Jews, there was a man called Samuel Ibn Adijah. He was a great warrior and also a great poet.

In beautiful poems, he told the Arabs what a wonderful nation the Jews were. And in Arabic, the language of the Arabs, he told them what the Jews hoped to do in the future.

Samuel was a very rich man. He lived in a beautiful castle which was painted in many colors, and which had heavy, thick walls all around it.

One day it happened that an Arabian Prince had quarreled with his enemies. The enemies became so angry that they wanted to kill the Prince. They got up an army to fight against him. Even the Prince's best friends were afraid to side with him so they, too, left him. Soon the Prince found himself all alone, with only his daughter and his cousin to stand by him. He had heard, however, of Samuel, the great Jewish warrior.

"I will go to this Jewish warrior, Samuel Ibn Adijah," said the Prince to his daughter and to his cousin. "They say he is a fine man, besides being a great warrior. Maybe he will help me."

So, with his daughter and his cousin as his only companions, he came to Samuel, who received him kindly and protected him from all his enemies.

Some time afterwards, the Prince left Samuel in order to try to win back his kingdom. But before leaving for his mission, he entrusted to Samuel his daughter, his cousin, and all of his arms. The Prince said:

"I know, my friend, that no one will keep my daughter and cousin, and my armor more safely than you. Good-bye, I hope everything will go well until I return."

Every day, Samuel and his little son, the Prince's daughter and her cousin would walk through the beautiful gardens of Samuel's palace. Every day they would await the return of the Prince. Every day Samuel would tell the Prince's daughter not to worry, that her father would surely return. But he himself felt that the Prince must have been killed. In truth the Prince never did return.

Instead, the enemies of the Prince came upon Samuel. They surrounded his castle with their horses and their big army. With wild cries they commanded him to bring forth the Prince's daughter and his armor.

"Give us the Prince's daughter and his armor—or—or," they shouted. "If you don't——"

Just then, Samuel's little son ran out of the castle.

"Oh, look, Grazia," he clapped his hands with joy

and excitement, as he called to his nurse, "look at all those soldiers!"

Before he knew it, the wild soldiers had seized him and cried:

"If you don't—we will kill your son right here. Yes, right before your eyes. Now you can choose. Either you give up the Prince's daughter or see your son killed."

Samuel could hardly believe his ears. He was stunned but for a little while only. Quickly he answered:

"No, I must protect the Prince's daughter, at any cost. She was placed in my trust and I must not give her up. It is better that I lose my son than that I lose my honor."

No sooner had Samuel announced his decision, than the cruel soldiers killed the boy right before his eyes.

Ever after, Samuel was called "The Faithful Samuel." And whenever the Arabs want to say that someone can be trusted, that he is very faithful—they say:

"Why, that man—he is as faithful as Samuel."

Did you ever know anybody as faithful as that?

THE LAW IS KIND

"O DEAR me, I've done it again! Again I have poured the milk into that *fleischig* (meat) pot. (You know that many Jews keep their meat dishes separate from their milk dishes.) Since Aaron has become sick, I have simply lost my head. I don't seem to remember anything. I just don't know what I am about."

Suddenly Peninah ran into the child's bedroom. She thought that little Aaron had called her. But she found him sleeping rather quietly. For the past three days, Aaron had been very sick. The doctor had ordered a fresh mustard-plaster every three hours on the boy's chest.

Peninah ran back to the kitchen, just as her husband was entering the house.

"I'm so glad you've come," she said. "Aaron is sleeping. Now I can run over to the College to ask them about the pot that I made *tref*. And at the same time I can find out if I may make the plasters for Aaron tomorrow even if it is the Sabbath."

"All right. Go ahead and don't worry. I am here. Watch where you are going and don't be so upset," Peninah's husband said kindly.

When Peninah came into the school at Sura, all the students were seated and were discussing various questions.

As Peninah was ushered in by the doorkeeper, they stopped talking. Saadiah, the Head Gaon or president, asked her:

"What is the matter? What brings you here, my dear woman?"

Peninah could hardly catch her breath, for she had been running all the way.

"You will excuse me for running in this way," Peninah said as she sat down, "but you see, my little son is sick at home. And I do want to rush back to him. Since he became sick, I hardly have a *kosher* pot left in the house. When I should take a *fleischig* pot and spoon, I take a *milchig* (milk) one. When I should take a *milchig* pot, I take a *fleischig* one. Now I would like you to tell me whether I am to throw away all those dishes."

Saadiah thought a while and then turned to the assembly and asked:

"What do you folks think about that?" One scholar arose and said:

"It's not for us to say one way or another. Let us look up and see what the rabbis teach us about such matters."

At this point a rather stern-looking man asked to be allowed to speak. As he arose, he looked around impatiently. Saadiah called the assembly to order. "We will now hear what Anan ben David, the Karaite, has to say," he said.

In a very low voice, Anan began. "My friends," he said, "this way of doing things is becoming too tiresome. Let us look up what the rabbis say,—and again let us look up what the rabbis say! Have we not the Bible? Can't we read what the Bible says? The Bible says very clearly:

" 'You shall not cook the kid in its mother's milk.' That, my friends, means exactly what it says. It's bad enough that you have to be cruel and kill the little lamb. Then, after that, don't go and cook it in its mother's milk. The laws in our Bible are very kind, my friends—very kind. They have nothing to do with dishes. You may cook meat in the one pot. Then take that same pot and boil milk in it. But, the Bible says, don't cook the two at the same time. Don't boil the kid in its mother's milk."

Peninah sat by quietly and listened. But she became very impatient in her eagerness to get back. And besides, she didn't understand what Anan was trying to show. She arose and quietly said to Saadiah:

"Please, Gaon, please. All I want to know is whether or not I must throw all those pots away. That's all."

The Karaite looked even sterner than before. He was about to say something to the woman, but Saadiah turned to her and again very kindly said:

"That is just what Anan is trying to tell us. According to him, there is no *milchig* and no *fleischig,* so you can just keep all your dishes."

"But, don't I have to do anything to make them *kosher* again?" the woman asked in surprise.

"Don't you see, my dear woman, nothing is *tref* because there is no *fleischig* or *milchig.*"

"I'm afraid, I don't understand what Anan is saying. Does he expect me to eat *tref* and spoil my whole household?" The woman spoke in an angry tone and shut her lips very tightly, as she finished talking.

"Please sit down again and we will soon tell you just what you have to do," Saadiah said.

Then he turned to the assembly and said:

"I am sorry that I cannot agree with Anan the

Karaite. Of course, we know what is written in the Bible. And we must make sure that we do know it. But we must also know how the rabbis have explained it. Then we shall be able to help this woman and others, too."

Another scholar arose and began to explain the law:

"Not to boil the kid in the mother's milk, means to have separate dishes for *milchig* and *fleischig*. That is what the rabbis here taught us. Now then, if this woman poured her milk into the *fleischig* pot, she must throw that pot away."

At this point Saadiah Gaon interrupted again and said:

"No, my dear friend. Now that we know what the Bible has written down, now that we know what the rabbis taught, we can judge this case.

"We agree that the pot is *tref*. It cannot be used as it is. But neither does it have to be thrown away."

Turning to Peninah he said:

"You throw a red hot stone into that pot and pour water over it. Then you may use the pot again. It shall be *kosher* again."

That decision Peninah understood. She thanked the scholars very much. Peninah was just about to rush out, when she stopped and said:

"O yes, I almost forgot. Since I am here I might as well ask you everything."

"Surely, surely," Saadiah said kindly. "We shall be glad to answer you."

"You see, my Aaron has a very bad cough. The doctor ordered that we put a mustard plaster on his chest every three hours. Now may I make the plasters on the Sabbath?"

"What!" again called the Karaite. "On the Sabbath. To work on the Sabbath! Of course, you are not allowed to make a plaster on the Sabbath."

"But he is so sick—so sick, and the plaster keeps him from coughing," the woman begged.

"That would make no difference. The Bible says you must not work on the Sabbath. You must work to make a plaster. Therefore it is settled. You may not make a plaster on the Sabbath."

"But maybe the rabbis can find a way of explaining the law. Maybe to do it for a sick person wouldn't really be working," Peninah pleaded. She had already learned something from the other decision and she was hopeful.

"You are right, my dear woman," Saadiah said kindly. "The rabbis teach us that the Sabbath is not to be considered when the welfare of the sick is concerned."

The Law Is Kind

"Oh, I knew the law would be kind," said the woman as she dried her tears.

Peninah thanked the scholars and quickly rushed home to Aaron. As she came into the house, she found Aaron sitting up, drinking some milk.

"God is good," Peninah cried for joy. "It seems the child is getting better and I shall not have to make the plasters on the Sabbath after all." Then she quickly ran into the kitchen to *kosher* her pots.

Aaron became well. When he grew up, his mother sent him to study in the School of Saadiah, the Gaon, where he too learned to explain the Torah.

EVEN THOUGH I LOSE

IN THE DAYS of Saadiah Gaon, a rich man lived in Babylonia. This rich man had two sons, whose names were Uri and Naphtali. One day the rich man died suddenly, and left no will. Who would now get all the money that the rich man had left? Would it be Uri or Naphtali?

The law of the land was that each son was to get an equal share. But Uri, the older son, did not like this idea. "Here is a chance to get very, very rich," he thought. So without a word to anyone he went to the Head of the Jews and said:

"When the case comes up between my brother and me, will you rule that all the money is to go to the older son? If you do this, I will make you a rich man. Think of it! Just by giving a little different explanation, you can become a very rich man."

"Let me think it over," said the Prince.

Even Though I Lose

The Prince put his hand to his forehead and sat thinking very hard. At last he said:

"All right, that's agreed."

Uri left, feeling very happy.

The Prince, however, could not eat nor could he sleep. Every minute he was thinking: "I am going to give an unfair decision. I am going to take away from Naphtali what rightfully belongs to him." Yet he was happy too, for he was also thinking: "In a few weeks I shall be a very rich man." But his conscience kept on troubling him so that he could not rest at all. At last he found a way of making his decision seem less wicked. He would have the Geonim agree in writing that his decision was just.

So the Prince sent messengers to get the signatures of the Geonim. When the Geonim saw the decision they were very much surprised. And they wondered what could have come over the Prince. One did not dare to ask any questions. He was told to sign, and sign he did.

Since Saadiah was the other Gaon at that time, he, too, was asked to sign the decision, but he refused to do so. He said that justice was justice and not even the Prince could make him say that that ruling was right.

"Saadiah," his friends warned, "don't be so stubborn. Don't you know you will lose your office?"

"Suppose I do," said Saadiah firmly, "is that a good reason for giving an unfair decision?" And Saadiah did not sign the note.

On the following day, Saadiah was removed from his office.

A good many years had passed. Saadiah was again put back into office. The Prince, who was Saadiah's enemy, was very old, and a new prince was to be put at the head of the Jews. Who would be chosen? Saadiah did not think of himself, nor of his enemy. Saadiah thought only of what would be good for the Jewish people. He decided that his enemy's son was a brave and just man, and that he should be chosen as the Prince. Therefore, Saadiah did all he could to have his enemy's son made Prince.

Many more years passed, and the young Prince died. Then Saadiah took the son of the Prince into his own home. There Saadiah educated him, just as he would have educated his own son. He prepared him to be Prince just as his father and grandfather had been before him. In this way, Saadiah did all he could even for a man who was his enemy. That was the kind of a man Saadiah was.

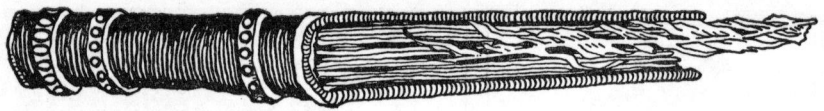

A GIFT TO THE CALIPH

It was a very hot day in Spain. Hasdai, dressed in expensive silks, a turban on his head, sat in the court of the Caliph. He was receiving ambassadors from countries far, far away. Though Hasdai was a Jew, he held a very high position in the government. He was just about to lie back in his plush chair when the courtier announced:

"The Ambassadors from Constantine of Rome!"

"Oh, the Ambassadors from Rome!" Hasdai became greatly excited. He ordered his servants to tidy up the room and put back a few chairs into their proper places. He, himself, arranged some books and papers on his desk, brushed some white spots off his coat, and then said:

"Very well, usher them in."

After the ambassadors had greeted Hasdai, they said:

"We have brought a very, very precious book to the Caliph. This is the Great Book of Cures. It tells how to cure every illness."

The doctors of Spain had always hoped to get this book. Now here it was at last!

A Gift to the Caliph

Hasdai was very well pleased to receive the book. He spoke to the ambassadors about many things, for Hasdai was interested in many things, but especially in his fellow-Jews all over the world. So after he had been talking to the ambassadors for some time, he asked:

"Do you know anything about the Jews in Rome? How are they being treated there?" But these ambassadors knew nothing about the Jews. So Hasdai learned nothing from them. After a while the ambassadors left.

Hasdai picked up the Book of Cures very carefully and took it into the Caliph's room. Placing the book before the Caliph, Hasdai said rather proudly:

"This is the great Book of Cures, which Constantine has kindly sent to Your Majesty."

The Caliph ordered all the physicians and great men of the court to come in. They were all happy to hear the good news. But soon one of them said:

"It is all very well to have the Book, but who will explain it to us? We cannot read Greek."

"That's right, that's right," a few other men chimed in, scratching their heads.

"We do not understand Greek."

For a while all were silent. Then the Caliph spoke:

A Gift to the Caliph

"Surely Constantine has a monk who can translate it for us. We will ask him to please send us some one to translate the Book of Cures."

Constantine, very happy to secure the good-will of the Caliph, immediately sent him a monk.

When the translator arrived, the Caliph again held court for the physicians and the wise men. Eagerly they all sat down to listen to the learned man. But to their surprise, he took the book in his hands, arose, and began to blush and stammer.

"I'm sorry, I do not understand your language well enough to translate this book into Arabic. However, I can translate it into Latin."

Those assembled were so disappointed that they could not speak. What was the use of this wonderful book if they could not understand it? Suddenly a voice broke the silence with "Let him translate it into Latin." It was Hasdai speaking.

"You surprise me, Hasdai," said the Caliph, puzzled. "Of what help will that be? The only language we understand is Arabic."

"Yes, your Majesty; but, if you will allow me, I can translate it into Arabic from the Latin," Hasdai said modestly.

Think of it! Of all the men in the court, Hasdai, the Jew, was the only one who understood Latin. So it was Hasdai who translated the famous Book of Cures into Arabic.

Though Hasdai was busy translating the book, he nevertheless continued to receive ambassadors. One day, ambassadors from Khorasan came to see Hasdai. As it was his habit to inquire about the Jews of strange lands, Hasdai asked them:

"Do you know how the Jews are faring in the Khorasan country?"

"There aren't any Jews in Khorasan, but in the land of the Kazars there is a Jewish king on the throne," the ambassadors told Hasdai.

"Is that true?" asked Hasdai, with great joy. "What kind of people are they? What language do they speak?"

"We are sorry, we can't answer your questions. But we shall be glad to deliver a message from you to their king." And so Hasdai wrote a beautiful letter in Hebrew. He told the king of the Kazars:

"The Jews in Spain are very rich, and they are learned too. They have a large college where great men come to teach. Will you please write and tell me all about the Jews of your country?"

The king of the Kazars wrote back this interesting story. Do you want to hear it?

THE CHOICE

ONCE there lived in Russia a very fierce race of people, called Kazars. They were very warlike all the time. So their kings went from country to country fighting with the people. All the nations feared them.

These rough people hardly had any religion at all, but on their travels they met Christians, Moslems, and Jews. When Bulan, one of their kings, met these people and learned about their religions, he became greatly dissatisfied with his own.

Day after day Bulan thought about it. One time when he was greatly worried, he dreamed a dream. It seemed to him that an angel came to him and said:

"You do not serve God in the right way. Send for a Jew, a Christian and a Moslem. Let them each explain his religion to you. Then you will choose the best for your own."

The angel disappeared and Bulan awoke. He

ordered that one of his wise men should come to him at once. The wise man was tired and sleepy. Why should he be taken out of his bed at night? But the king's orders must be obeyed. Therefore he dressed quickly and came before Bulan.

Then Bulan spoke to him and said:

> *"Tell me, Wise One,*
> *Tell me true,*
> *What does your God*
> *Mean to you?"*

Answered the Wise Man:

> *"God is a Spirit,*
> *Far removed is He,*
> *How can He care*
> *For you or for me?"*

Bulan was not satisfied with this explanation.

"Bah," he said. "No—no. A god who does not guard over my kingdom, a god who does not care about me, can't be my God."

A few days later, Bulan ordered that a Christian monk should come to him. When the monk entered in his long black gown and three-cornered hat of the same color, Bulan was interested.

Again he said:

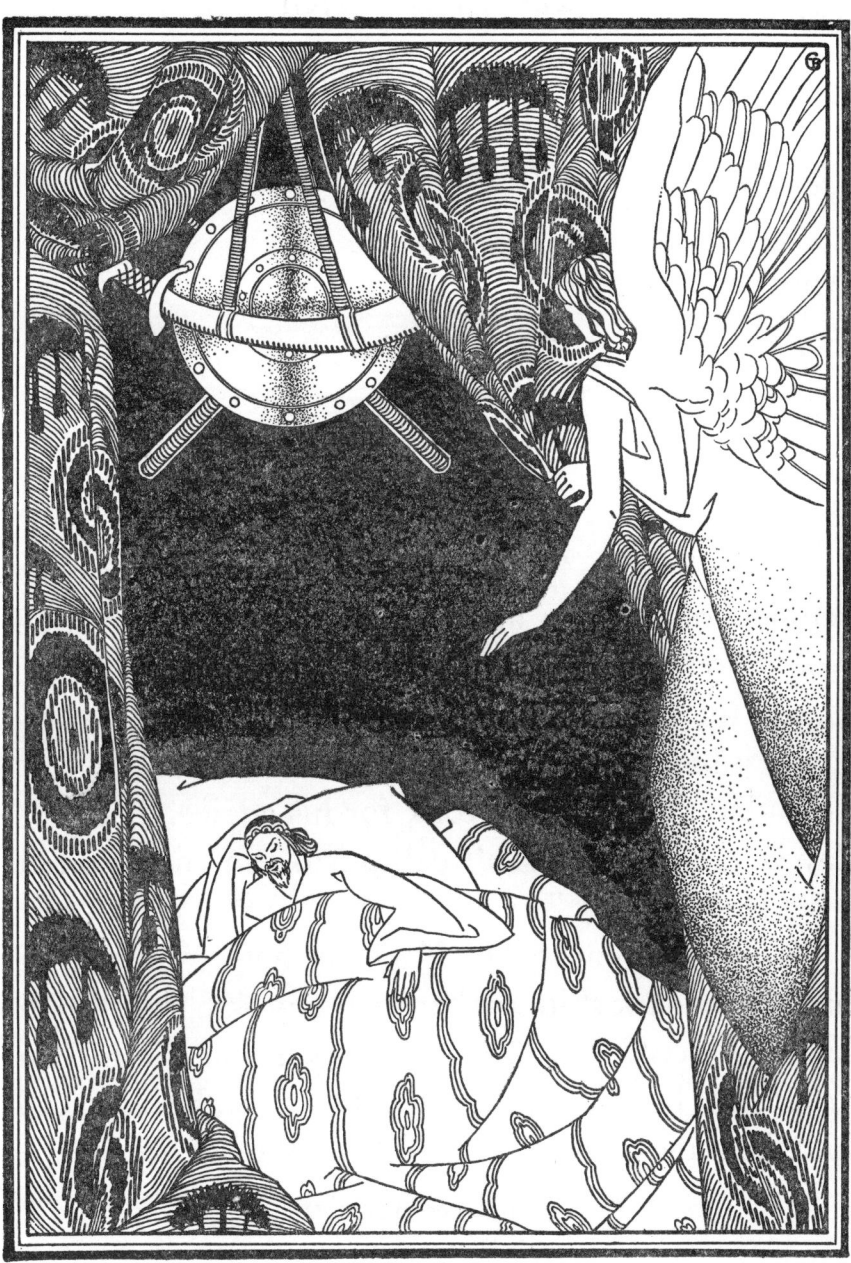

> *"Tell me Monk,*
> *Tell me true,*
> *What religion*
> *Pleases you?"*

Answered the Monk:

> *"My religion*
> *As you see,*
> *My religion*
> *Pleases me."*

Bulan asked: "If you had to choose between the religion of the Jew and that of the Moslem, which would you choose?" The Monk answered: "I would choose the Jewish religion. It is the oldest, and our religion is based on it."

Bulan thanked the Monk for his advice. The next day Bulan said: "I shall call a Moslem and find out what he has to say."

So the next day, a Moslem came before Bulan. He had a very dark skin, darker than any skin that Bulan had ever seen. His long grey gown and the turban around his head made him very attractive. Bulan asked him the same question that he had asked of the others.

> *"Tell me Moslem,*
> *Tell me true,*

*Which religion
Pleases you?"*

Answered the Moslem:

*"My religion
As you see,
My religion
Pleases me."*

"If you had to choose between the religion of the Jew, and that of the Monk, which would you choose?"

The Moslem answered: "I would choose the Jewish religion. It is the oldest, and our religion is based on it." Bulan thanked him for his advice. The next day he called a Jew and put his question:

*"Tell me Jew,
Tell me true,
Which religion
Pleases you?"*

The Jew answered:

*"My religion
As you see,
My religion
Pleases me."*

Bulan asked:

*"Tell me Jew,
Tell me true,
What does God
Mean to you?"*

The Jew answered:

*"Love thy neighbor as thyself
And know the prophets too.
This, the message of the Jew
Forever will be true."*

Bulan then turned to the Jew and said: "You will be happy to know that I asked the Monk this question: 'If you had to choose between the religion of the Jew and that of the Moslem, which would you choose?' He answered: 'The Jewish religion.' I then asked the Moslem a similar question. He answered: 'The Jewish religion.' Now, all religions seem good to me if they teach us that there is one God who is the Father of us all, and that all men are brothers. But as the Jewish religion is the oldest, my folk and I shall come to you."

"So Bulan and his people became Jews. And I am one of his great-great-grandchildren," the king of the Kazars wrote.

The story pleased Hasdai very much. It gave him courage to help the Jews of Spain to become greater and greater.

THE SLAVE RABBI

THERE were once two great Jewish colleges in Sura and Pumpeditha, famous cities in Babylonia. It was in one of these colleges that Saadiah was Gaon. When people had a quarrel and could not make peace, where do you think they went? To Babylonia. For, this great college also served as a court. When a man wanted to become a rabbi, where do you think he went? To Babylonia.

A time came, however, when the Jews stopped sending their students to Babylonia. Little by little Babylonia was losing its greatness. It seemed as if all the work that had been done there would be lost. What was to be done? The Babylonian Jews, very much worried, called a meeting of all the rabbis and all the important people. The question was: "What should be done to keep up the great learning which had been started in Babylonia?" Some said:

The Slave Rabbi

"Send out letters to all the countries where Jews live. Tell them what great colleges we have here, and ask them for the sake of Jewish learning to help support these colleges. Tell them that otherwise all the good work of the rabbis will be lost. The schools will have to be closed."

"No, no," said others. "Don't send letters. Send people. Send our very own great scholars."

So they decided to send out four of their greatest scholars to different parts of the world. They were to assemble Jews wherever they went and say to them:

"We have fine schools and colleges in Babylon. You remember that when Johanan ben Zakkai risked his life to go before Vespasian, he asked for only one thing—to build a little school.

"Now that we have all these great and fine colleges there, will you allow them to be closed? If you do not send your students and your great scholars to Babylonia—that is what will surely happen."

So, in accordance with this plan, these four great scholars started out from Babylonia. On their travels they had to cross a big sea. On this sea there were many pirates who fell on the vessel on which the rabbis were sailing. The pirates captured the four rabbis and carried them off to slave markets. Two of them were taken to Africa, the third to France, and the fourth to Spain. Was this to be the end of the rabbis and the schools in Babylon? Would the schools have to be closed after all? Would these great rabbis be sold as slaves? Was this to be the sad end of such well-laid plans?

In those days every country had a market place where the rich people came to buy their slaves. To these market places the rabbis were brought. And these old, learned men were placed on the block, on show, where everybody could see them. These old rabbis, loved and honored by the Jewish people, were put up for sale just like sheep or cows or horses. Can you imagine the shame and sorrow these men felt?

The pirates, however, were very happy. Now they would get rich! These Jewish men were worth thousands of dollars. In Spain the captain of the pirates stepped up on the platform and called out:

"Hear ye; hear ye. Here we have an extraordinary slave, but of course he is very expensive. It isn't every day that we can offer you slaves as fine as this one."

There was great excitement in the market place. The Jews and even the Gentiles were greatly astonished. How had these pirates succeeded in capturing a great rabbi? What! A rabbi to be sold as a slave! What a disgrace, they cried. It all seemed so impossible. A cry of horror arose from the Jews. No, they would never allow it. That would be terrible!

Meanwhile the pirate cried again:

"Well, what am I offered for this one? A great man, a great scholar. Tested him myself." At that the stupid crowd began to laugh. "What am I bid? Guaranteed to know everything!" the pirate continued.

Jews and Gentiles alike could not bear to hear the pirate poke fun at the great rabbi. The Gentiles offered high prices, but the Jews always added to the offers. The Jews had made up their minds not to let the rabbi be sold into slavery. To their joy, they did at last buy freedom for this highly respected man.

Among the bidders in the slave market was a man whose name you have heard before. Yes, that man was the famous Jewish scholar, Hasdai. When Rabbi ben Enoch was put up on the platform, Hasdai offered a larger price for him than anybody else there, so that he was sold to Hasdai. I don't know whether you can imagine how happy Hasdai was. For surely, you don't think that he had bought the rabbi for his slave! Hasdai was happy because he knew that God had sent him a great treasure. He knew that no amount of money could pay for that treasure. The first thing that Hasdai did was to give Rabbi ben Enoch his liberty. Then, when Rabbi ben Enoch had told him the whole story of his mission, Hasdai offered to help him accomplish what he had set out to do. He took the learned Rabbi ben Enoch with him to the college in Spain.

The rabbis who had been taken to the other countries were freed, too.

Can you imagine how happy the rabbis were to be free again? So their trouble had not been in vain. Their hopes would be fulfilled. The work at Babylonia would not be wasted.

Moses ben Enoch was so anxious to do his duty that he did not stop even to take off his slave's clothes. As soon as he was set free, he went to the college with Hasdai at once. There he asked Hasdai to let him stand near the door and listen to the discussion. No one noticed him at all. He had been standing there some time when a very hard problem came up. It was so difficult that even the head of the college could not solve it.

Suddenly a voice was heard asking:

"May I please try to answer the question?"

Everybody turned to see who was talking. Can you imagine their surprise when they saw a slave in the school? And not only that, but the slave trying to answer a question—and such a hard one at that.

"That must be some slave who has gone out of his mind," a number of scholars said. But the head of the college being wiser than they, in his usual polite way, asked Ben Enoch to come up to the front. When he had modestly done so, quietly and slowly, he answered the question.

Seeing how wise Ben Enoch was, the head of the college said:

"So wise a man should take my place, for he knows more than I do." So Moses ben Enoch, this rabbi from Babylonia, became the head of the college in Spain.

Hasdai went up to the head of the college and asked his permission to speak to the Assembly and Hasdai told the whole story of Rabbi Moses ben Enoch.

Now, when a man wanted to become a rabbi, where do you think he went? To Spain, of course. When people quarreled and could not make peace with each other, where did they go? To Spain. And so Spain took the place of Babylonia as the center of Jewish living and of Jewish learning.

THE WONDROUS TREE

"Very warm night again, isn't it?" remarked the Arabian poet.

"Yes, very warm indeed," smilingly answered the Jewish shopkeeper to whom the remark had been made, "but a poet shouldn't mind warm nights. The warm nights in Spain are so beautiful—they make it easier to write poetry."

"You are only joking. But I tell you, the only ones who don't have to worry are you Spanish Jews. You are richer than the Jews of the rest of the world. You can do as you please during the entire year."

"Yes, I suppose most of us can," answered the shopkeeper thoughtfully.

"You are well treated. You can worship as you please," continued the Arabian poet, "you are very learned and best of all, you have great poets among you."

The Wondrous Tree 145

The Arabian poet seemed jealous. There was an odd gleam in his eyes. He had suddenly become silent, to the surprise of the Jewish shopkeeper. After a long pause, the poet went over to the counter and said:

"Let me have a pad of paper, even though I think it is too hot to work."

"I'll tell you," the Arabian poet continued with a strange twinkle in his eye, "I can write you a poem for your Ibn Gabirol anyway." And as he spoke, he wrote this on the pad:

*"Ibn Gabirol—a great Jewish poet is he,
But Ibn Gabirol a great poet must not be."*

The Arabian laughed loudly, and threw the piece of paper on the counter.

"Here, keep it," he said, "I usually get paid for my poems, but you don't have to pay me for this one." With these last words he walked out of the store.

"I wonder what he means by all that?" said the shopkeeper's wife.

"Oh, nothing! He's just jealous of us Jews. They all are. And since he is a poet—he is especially jealous of Gabirol."

"I'll keep these lines," said the shopkeeper's wife, as she picked up the paper from the counter and read again:

> *"Gabirol, a great Jewish poet is he,*
> *But Gabirol a great poet must not be."*

"I wonder what he means," she repeated as she folded the paper and put it in one of her bureau drawers.

Several years had passed after this incident. Gabirol, the great Jewish poet, had suddenly disappeared. No one knew what had happened to him. No trace could be found of the great poet. The shopkeeper had forgotten about the poem the Arabian poet had given him. In fact, he would have forgotten about the poet, but for a strange thing. In front of that poet's house a wonderfully beautiful tree had sprung up.

The organ-grinders in the street played:

> *"I passed a little fig tree,*
> *With buds so beautiful to see,*
> *And I am sure, oh, very sure*
> *There is a fairy in that tree."*

And the children sang:

> *"Its fruit is long,*
> *Yes, very long,*
> *And anyone who eats it*
> *Gets very wise*
> *And very strong,*

Yes, very wise
And very strong."

Poor people, rich people, grown-up men and grown-up women, little boys and little girls, all went to see the beautiful tree. Even the Caliph learned about this Wondrous Tree, this tree that was growing in front of the Arabian poet's house.

The king's servants all cried:

"A fairy is hidden in it! Surely a fairy is hidden in it."

"We shall go and find out for ourselves," said the Caliph.

And off he started with a laborer armed with a spade. When they came to the Wondrous Tree, the man began to dig deep, deep under it. From every part of the town the people came to watch the digging. Breathlessly they looked on. With every spadeful, a cry of wonderment went up. Suddenly the laborer became pale.

"Look, look!" he exclaimed to the King. "Look, someone is buried here!"

The king ordered the body to be taken up, out of its grave.

"Lord, have mercy," the people all cried as the body was lifted up. "Who can it be? A man buried under that tree!" Some of the king's courtiers, however, had already recognized the face of the dead man.

But they looked again, and again.

"Yes, yes, that is so. It is the body of Gabirol, the Jewish poet!" they exclaimed with horror.

Now you remember the Jewish shopkeeper, for whom the Arabian had written that poem about Ibn Gabirol? That shopkeeper too had come to watch the digging under the Wondrous Tree.

When he saw the body of Gabirol he began to tremble. Oh, he saw it all now! It all came back to him. That hot summer night—and the poem the Arabian had thrown over the counter. The poem read:

> "Gabirol a great Jewish poet is he,
> But Gabirol a great poet must not be."

So the Arabian meant that he would kill Ibn Gabirol. And the shopkeeper kept shaking his head and mumbling to himself:

"'Ibn Gabirol a great Jewish poet must not be.' Who would have thought it—who would have thought it!"

"Guess the Arabian is sorry he said so much to me that night," the shopkeeper thought to himself. Suddenly he began to push through the crowd.

"Let me pass, please. Quickly, quickly, let me

pass. I have something very important to tell the king," he said as he elbowed his way through the crowd. "I know who committed this crime; I tell you, I know!" the shopkeeper kept shouting as he came up to the Caliph.

"Your Majesty, I know who killed Ibn Gabirol. I am sure of it. It was this man," and he pointed to the Arabian poet who was standing in the crowd.

"Be careful what you say," the Caliph answered sternly. "Can you prove it?"

"I can, I can." The shopkeeper would not be quieted.

"Very well then, go ahead," said the Caliph.

"About three years ago at this time," the shopkeeper went on, "the Arabian poet came to my store to buy some paper. He sat there a long time and spoke to me about the Jews in Spain. He thought they were getting altogether too great and too rich. Then he turned to me and laughingly said:

" 'Here, I will write you a poem for your Ibn Gabirol.' And he wrote something like this:

" 'Ibn Gabirol is a great poet, but he won't remain a great poet.' If I'm not mistaken my wife still has the piece of paper."

"He lies, he lies!" cried the Arabian, turning white.

The Wondrous Tree

"Go get that paper," commanded the Caliph.

In a few minutes, the shopkeeper returned.

"Here's the poem," said he. "See for yourself."

"That's not my handwriting. That Jew is just trying to get me into trouble. Believe me, O Caliph, believe me!" the Arabian begged.

"Well," said the Caliph, after he had thought a few minutes. "We shall see. Here is a piece of paper," he said, turning to the poet. "Write down: 'I have not killed Ibn Gabirol.'" The Arabian poet wrote as directed, but his hand trembled. He tried to disguise his handwriting but he couldn't. Everyone could see that it was the same handwriting. The Caliph believed it, too.

"Get the bamboo stick," he ordered. "You shall be whipped until you tell the whole truth."

For some time, the poet would not speak, but at last the pain became too great to bear, and the Arabian cried out:

"Yes, it's true. It's true. I killed that Ibn Gabirol. Lord, how I hated him! I hated him because he was such a wonderful poet. One night I asked him to come to visit me. He did. We spoke of the great mercy of his Jewish God." The Arabian poet looked far, far away. It seemed he was trying to think of how Gabirol looked that night.

"Gabirol said, 'Forget yourself. Think only of God. If everybody would do that—this world would be beautiful.'

"Just then I fell upon him and I killed him. Quietly I buried him under the trees. No one heard us. Only his God—and the stars looked on. But his cursed blood sent forth beautiful fruit on this tree. Even though I had killed him, he lived on right before my eyes. And his poems, even more beautiful than this tree, live on and on forever. You know the rest," and as he spoke the Arabian fell to the earth, exhausted from pain.

Then the people mourned:

> *"Alas, alas, we've learned it,*
> *The secret of this tree;*
> *The blood of Gabirol fed it,*
> *So, beautiful it must be."*

The Arabian was hanged. And Ibn Gabirol, whom he had slain, lives on forever and ever because of his beautiful poems.

IN THE EAST IS MY HEART

"Let's play school and I will be teacher," said Miriam, a dark-haired little girl.

"No, no, play making bricks in Egypt."

"Oh, I don't want to think of the Jews in Egypt."

"Better play 'Going to Jerusalem,'" said Judah, a little boy of ten.

"Don't you ever get tired of that game, Judah? After all that playing and marching, you could be in Jerusalem by now."

"I am going to Jerusalem some day," Judah answered proudly. His eyes filled up with tears. Oh, how he wanted to go to Jerusalem! "All right, let's play 'Going to Jerusalem.' You know how the game is played."

The children began to march around chairs. At the end of each round some child was left out. Someone stayed behind. Someone did not reach

In the East Is My Heart

Jerusalem. Who do you think did get to Jerusalem? Who do you think won the game? No, it was not Judah, not yet. Not even in the game did he get his wish fulfilled. Miriam won the game.

That evening at the table his father asked Judah kindly:

"Well, Judah, did you get to Jerusalem yet?" Judah hung his head.

"No," he answered sadly, "not yet, but I will some day."

Many days passed. Then many years. Judah grew up and went to college in Spain. One day Judah, now tall and handsome, was sitting on a big rock, facing east and writing a poem. He looked up and recited:

> *"O city, far-off East, the beautiful,*
> *The blest,*
> *My Spirit longs for thee*
> *From out the far-off West.*
> *If only I had an eagle's wings,*
> *Straight would I fly to thee,*
> *And I would moisten thy holy dust*
> *With tears ever running free."* [1]

Some of his college friends came over and listened.

---
[1] Adapted from the translation by Emma Lazarus.

"Well, Judah," said one, "are you studying hard for the doctor's exam?"

"Oh, bother! Exam!" replied Judah angrily. "I'm writing poetry to my beloved."

His friends drew back, surprised. So Judah had a girl! They didn't know that.

When Judah saw their surprise he asked:

"Want to hear one of the poems? How do you like this one?

> "*O city, far-off East, the beautiful, the blest,*
> *My Spirit longs for thee*
> *From out the far-off West.*
> *If only I had an eagle's wings,*
> *Straight would I fly to thee,*
> *And I would moisten thy holy dust*
> *With tears ever running free.*"

The friends all agreed that the poem was beautiful. They saw their mistake. Judah had no real girl. His girl was Jerusalem.

"Please read us another one," they begged. And they didn't have to coax Judah. Immediately he began:

> "*In the East, in the East*
> *Is my heart,*
> *And I dwell in the end of the West.*
> *All the beauties and treasures of Spain*

*Are worthless as dust
In mine eyes;
But the dust of the ruined Temple
As a treasure of beauty I prize.*"[1]

When he finished reading, one of the boys said:

"Beautiful poems—but how will that help you pass the exam?"

"That's true," sighed Judah. "Thinking and dreaming and writing of the Holy Land won't help me pass the exams. And I do want to become a doctor. I shall earn a lot of money and then I shall go to my beloved city, Jerusalem."

Judah was graduated from college. He became a very successful doctor. He was so busy that he hardly found time to write poems to his beloved.

Years passed. Judah married and had one daughter. As soon as she could speak she, too, sang songs about Erets Israel.

One day when she was about eight years old, she suddenly turned to her father and said:

"Father, I've heard so much about Jerusalem, and I know so many songs and poems about it, but I have never seen Jerusalem. Won't we ever go there?"

Then Judah took her on his knee, and told her at her age, he had always played "Going to Jerusalem,"

---

[1]Adapted from the translation by Emma Lazarus.

and how he, too, had made up his mind that when he grew up he would surely go there.

"Oh, how I long to go there now!" he ended. "But all my brothers and sisters are here and my dear friends, too. I hate to leave them all. And besides, your mother doesn't want to go."

More years passed. Judah already had a grandchild, and even his grandchild kept on singing:

> *"In the East, in the East,*
> *Is my heart,*
> *And I dwell in the end of the West.*
> *All the beauties and treasures of Spain*
> *Are just like the dust*
> *In mine eyes;*
> *But the dust of the ruined Temple*
> *As a treasure of beauty I prize."*

At last the day came when Judah could wait no longer. He tore himself away from his beloved family —his wife, his daughter, and his only grandchild. He left his many, many friends. He gave up his work as a doctor, and started for Jerusalem.

When Judah's ship was well out to sea, a strong wind arose which soon became a storm. The waves kept dashing higher and higher. The boat was tossed hither and thither. It seemed as though they would never reach the holy city. Days passed before the storm quieted down. At last, tired but hopeful, he arrived in the Holy Land.

Judah had worked, and worked, and waited. But at last he had his reward. Was this really Jerusalem? Was this really Judah in the streets of his beloved city? It didn't seem possible. It didn't seem true!

Judah visited the Cave of Macpelah, the Wailing Wall, Rachel's Tomb, and all the other places he so longed to see. He touched each building, each stone, with his hands to make sure that he wasn't dreaming. While on the boat, Judah had begun to write a book about Judaism, and many new poems. He was now able to finish his books in the place where he had always longed to be.

But Judah wasn't lucky enough to enjoy his beloved Jerusalem very long. Only a few months after he had reached the city, he was kneeling outside the city walls, chanting a song to Zion. While the great poet of Zion was singing his song, a Mohammedan horseman came along. When he saw Judah, a Jew, praying at the Wall, it made him very angry. So angry did he become that he fell upon Judah and killed him.

Now, I know you feel sorry for Judah. But don't forget that he did reach Jerusalem, his beloved city. And even to this day his poems to Zion are sung.

AN ANGEL DID IT

"It's hard to make a living in Spain. I think I'll try another country." So spoke Abraham Ibn Ezra to his mother. "But," he added, with a smile, "it seems I simply haven't any luck. If I were to begin to make shrouds, I'm sure men would stop dying, or if I were to make candles, the sun would not set until I gave up the candle trade."

His mother smiled a kind mother's smile; lightly tapping him on the shoulder, she answered:

"Now, don't speak that way, Abraham. You mustn't lose courage, my son. As you go from country to country you will surely find something at which you can make a good livelihood."

Abraham had just returned to Spain for a little visit with his mother. He had already been to Italy, France and England.

"But do you know, Mother," he said, "I think that

I like to travel from country to country just for the fun of traveling. I couldn't stay in one place, even if I could earn enough to live on there. It's so much more interesting to keep moving from place to place. Besides it helps me understand not only the Jews, but other people as well."

What answer could his mother give Abraham? She too, thought it was interesting to travel. However traveling takes time, you know. When you travel you don't have much time for anything else. But Abraham was so brilliant and so learned. He could do so much for his people, if he would only settle down to work in one place. If only he would give his time to one thing!

"Well," she heaved a heavy sigh, "maybe you will meet a nice girl, and you'll get married—and then you will stay in one place and really do something."

"Now, Mother, that isn't fair. You know I work all the time, and this explanation of the Bible which I am writing will be an important piece of work, I hope."

"This is the first time I have heard about it," his mother said. Her wrinkles seemed to smooth out and she looked quite pretty and young again. "Do tell me about it." She was very much excited.

"I don't know how interesting you will find it—but this is the idea.

"You know there were the great teachers who wrote explanations of the Bible but their explanations were altogether too long. They put all kinds of strange meanings into the Bible. Well, I will write an explanation of the Bible without putting fairy stories in it."

"Yes? What do you expect to do?" Abraham's mother asked. And the look in her eyes said:

"Please go on and tell me."

"You see, it's not such a short story. If you really care to listen, I will tell you."

"Why do you ask such foolish questions?" his mother said lovingly, as she bent over and kissed him.

Pleased, Abraham continued:

"Then you remember, Mother, there came the Karaites and they thought that every single letter in the Bible was important—every single letter. These Karaites said the rabbis had nothing to teach them at all. But I am trying to do this: First I find out what the rabbis wanted to teach us. Then I explain what is written in the Bible. But I am trying to do that in a clear, simple way. That is why I am working very hard to write this explanation."

"May God bless you, may God bless you," his mother said as she wiped away the tears from her eyes.

As he had promised his mother, Ibn Ezra did finish his explanation of the Bible. And so clear was

An Angel Did It

his explanation that young Jewish people began to study the Bible more carefully than ever before.

But his work did not stop Ibn Ezra from traveling. He went to Egypt, to Palestine, and to Babylon. In every country, he left behind the marks of his great learning. In this way he taught all the Jews about the great Spanish poets and philosophers. So it was a good thing after all that Ibn Ezra went from country to country.

Now Judah Halevi lived in Spain at the time when Ibn Ezra was traveling. It happened one day that Judah had been working for a whole day on a Purim song. He had almost finished the whole song, only he could not write the last line. He tried again and again but he simply couldn't find the right thought nor the right rhyme. He was quite upset. Just as he was straining every nerve to get that last line, his wife interrupted him with this:

"Judah, you may be a great poet, but you are not doing your duty as a father. We have only one daughter and you don't even take the trouble to find her a good husband."

Judah, tired and angry because he couldn't find a rhyme for his Purim song, called out in disgust:

"The first stranger that comes to the door can marry her. Will that please you?"

He had hardly finished saying these words when a knock was heard on the door.

Judah's wife went to open the door. What she saw made her knees sink under her. Before her stood a man in rags. He looked dirty and tired.

"Have you a room for a lodger over night? I have a long way to go and I am very far from an inn."

Judah's wife was thinking, "Good God, will my daughter have to marry this man?"

But what could she do? She couldn't refuse a lodging place to a stranger. Therefore she said, "Come in, we can find room," but her mind was troubled: "My daughter, my only child, will she have to marry this beggar? Can Judah mean it?"

As the stranger entered, he noticed that Judah was pacing up and down the room counting on his fingers and whispering to himself. Ibn Ezra (for it was he) knew at once that Judah was not talking to himself. It was clear to him that his host was counting the syllables of words for a poem.

"Judah, too, sometimes finds it hard to get a good rhyme," Ibn Ezra thought to himself.

Judah looked up for a second, greeted the stranger, and then continued whispering and counting to himself.

His wife, seeing that Judah had no intention of

speaking to the stranger, showed him his room and wished him good-night.

For some time Judah continued to work on his poem. But at last he gave up and he, too, went to sleep.

During the night Judah's wife could not sleep well because she was worried about her daughter. Did Judah really mean what he had said? And would he really make her daughter marry the ragged and ignorant beggar? She was hoping for the morning to come so they could talk the matter over.

Neither could Judah sleep because his Purim song was going through his head. Whenever he thought he had found the rhyme it always turned out wrong in the end. As they were lying in bed awake, each thinking and worrying, each thought he heard a noise in the study.

Quietly they both got up and watched him from a distance. To their surprise they saw the stranger sitting at the desk where the unfinished poem lay. They watched him closely as he sat there, thinking, the pen in his hand. Then they saw him write something and go back to his bed.

Then Judah and his wife both ran into the room, and there they saw Judah's song, beautifully finished! If they hadn't seen the stranger write it, they couldn't have believed it.

An Angel Did It

Judah picked up the paper. Suddenly he looked alarmed.

"What's wrong? What's troubling you, Judah?" his wife asked anxiously.

"There is something peculiar, something queer about this stranger," Judah answered. "Only an angel or Ibn Ezra, the young poet, could have finished this poem. And here it is, all finished, with a beautiful line and a beautiful rhyme. Didn't we both see the stranger do it?"

The sun had not yet risen, so Judah Halevi and his wife went back to bed. But again they couldn't sleep. This time it was because they were wondering who this stranger was. Could he really be the famous Abraham Ibn Ezra? If so, how fortunate for their daughter!

When at last the sun began to rise, Judah and his wife could hardly wait to get into their clothes.

They found the stranger in the sitting-room, in his *talith* and *tefillin,* praying. Judah put on his *talith* and prayed too. Judah's wife in the meantime quickly prepared some breakfast and set it on the table.

At breakfast, Judah Halevi said to the stranger:

"We hardly had a chance to ask your name last night."

"Why, I thought everybody knew the Wandering

Jew, Abraham Ibn Ezra," the young traveler in his beggar's clothes replied.

Judah and his wife stopped eating and both stood up in great surprise.

Extending his hand to Abraham, Judah said: "I told my wife that only Abraham Ibn Ezra or an angel could have finished that poem. You know we saw you write it last night."

Abraham flushed, as he said with a smile: "Well, I am not an angel, but they do call me Abraham Ibn Ezra."

Just then Judah's daughter came in. This was the right moment for Judah to tell Ibn Ezra as well as his daughter about his plans for their marriage.

"Listen, my daughter, and, you too, our dear guest, to a rash vow I made yesterday." He then told them the whole story. Both maid and man looked embarrassed; but, as you may guess, Ibn Ezra married Judah's daughter. And happily the two of them continued to travel.

THE DOCTOR ARRIVES

"The doctor is here! The doctor is here!" This was the cry that went ringing through the hall. Jews, Christians, Mohammedans, judges, bailiffs, common people, all were filled with great excitement. They had been waiting since the early morning. It was now late in the afternoon. But at last the doctor had arrived.

"Sh-sh—quiet—quiet. Can't you hear that the doctor has come?"

"I shall be with you all in a minute," Dr. Maimonides promised as he hurried past them.

"Only, please let me wash my hands and take a little bite."

Soon Dr. Maimonides came out and far into the night he sat treating his patients.

Every day, beginning early in the morning, Dr. Maimonides used to attend the great Saladin, Sultan of Egypt. He did not return home until noon, and often much later. And there his patients would be waiting for him.

As the people sat waiting for the doctor, you could hear them say:

"I knew his family in Spain," said one old man.

"Spain? What are you talking about? They came from Africa," remarked another.

"Yes, I know that," answered the old man, "they traveled through many countries—the Maimons did—until they settled here in Egypt. I remember one night I was at their home in Spain. Old Maimon was sitting with his son David, talking about the conditions in Spain. Old Maimon said:

" 'Who would believe it? Who would believe that this is Spain? This the country where Jehudah Halevi, Ibn Gabirol lived and worked? This the country where the Jews were so well treated; so rich and so learned? Is this the country where so many Jewish poets and philosophers were born?'

"The father of Moses Maimonides was thus half thinking to himself and half talking to his older son, David, who sat near by.

" 'Yes, Father. It seems there is no place where a Jew can feel safe now, no place where a Jew can serve his God freely. Shall we, too, have to become Mohammedans, as some of the other Jews have had to do?'

"Maimon closed his eyes and shuddered. 'No, no, God forbid,' he said, motioning with his hand as if to drive off evil.

" 'We should rather leave this home of ours. We shall go into exile—and we shall try to find a free country, a country where they will let us worship as we believe.'

" 'Where shall we go? When? We don't want little Moses to grow up in this country. It's true, I, myself, teach him the Bible and the Talmud and some arithmetic. Still he is studying medicine with the Mohammedan professors and they teach him their philosophy, and their religion. Soon he, too, may believe that Allah is God, and Mahomet his prophet. I have decided that we shall go to Southern Spain.' And so Maimon and his family left for Southern Spain.

Soon after they came there, the same African Mohammedans captured that place, too, and again the Maimon family had to begin to wander. This time they went to Africa. They hadn't been there very long when there, too, the Jews were made to take Islam for their religion. Many Jews learned the prayers and customs of the Mohammedans and became make-believe Mohammedans. But they made believe for so long that, in time, they forgot the truth. They forgot that they were Jews.

"Meanwhile little Moses had grown up to be a

brilliant man and a great scholar. In spite of all the traveling the family had to do, Moses never stopped studying. He never said, 'We went to Almeria so I couldn't study,' or 'We went to Fez, so I couldn't study.' No indeed, he not only studied, he even began to write a book.

"However, the Maimons did not stay long in Fez. At last they went to Egypt. Soon after they had settled there, Old Maimon died. Now Moses and his brother David had to support the family. They opened a big jewelry store, and traded with countries far, far away. David had more to do with the business than did Moses. It was David who traveled to the different countries to sell them the precious jewels. But on one of his journeys, David was drowned in the Indian Ocean, and after this, Moses had to take care of his own and his brother's families. By this time Moses had become a doctor. You remember that although in Spain he had begun to study medicine, his heart was in his Jewish studies. One day he said to his mother:

" 'It's too bad that I must be a doctor. I do wish I had more time to give to the writing of that book which I began in Spain.'

" 'Do you mean that book in which you explain

all the Jewish laws?' asked his mother kindly and proudly.

" 'Yes, that's it. I am trying to make it so simple that a Jew will be able to find any law very quickly.'

"So between being a doctor, and trying to support two families, Moses wrote this book to explain the Jewish laws.

"Little by little his fame as a doctor spread and he became busier, but Moses did not give up his writings. He worked every single minute of the day. And he didn't even have time to read a story book. He just worked and worked all the time."

Everybody had gathered around the old man and listened quietly, because they were all interested.

At last, another man said, "And do you think that, with all his work, he stopped writing?"

"Of course not. Don't you think I know of his greatest book? In that book he shows that there isn't much difference between Judaism and the philosophy of the Greeks," answered the old man, proud of all he knew.

By now some of the people were beginning to fall asleep—because they didn't know such big words—and they didn't know just what Maimonides wanted to prove.

But one of those who had been listening, asked:

"Is that what he called the 'Guide to the Perplexed?'" It was a young man talking. He was glad that he could understand everything the older men were talking about.

"Yes, and do you know that he has been asked to be court physician to Richard the Lion-hearted, the great king of England?"

"Oh, really," said an old lady. "How lovely! Where will he get the strength to do it all?"

"But he didn't accept that offer. He would rather give his time to his writings," answered the old man with the air of one who knows it all.

"And now there is a saying: From Moses to Moses, there has been none like Moses," the old man continued.

"What does that mean?" asked a young girl, who had been listening all the time.

"It means that from Moses who led the Jews out of Egypt till this Moses, Moses Maimonides, our doctor, no one has ever been as great as these two men." The man had just finished speaking when there was a sudden rush in the hall.

"Sh-sh—quiet—quiet. Can't you hear that the doctor has come in?"

TABLES TURNED

SALADIN, the Caliph of Egypt, came to like Moses Maimonides, the philosopher and physician, very much. Indeed, so much did the Caliph think of him that he told Moses all the secrets of the court. Therefore, all the courtiers became very jealous of Moses.

Now there was one courtier, Dijy, by name, who was so jealous of Moses that he began to stir up trouble against him. One day, when Dijy was alone with the Caliph, he began to talk about Moses in this manner:

"Your Highness," he said, "your Jewish physician may not be a traitor to the country, but I know he has said some very unpleasant things about you."

"Oh, Dijy, I have no time to waste listening to your nonsense," Saladin scolded the courtier. "You don't like Moses because he is a great man, a great philosopher, and a great physician. And what hurts you courtiers most of all is that he is a Jew." As he ended his speech the Caliph was about to go about his business. But, just then, Dijy looked about slyly and said:

"Well, perhaps you will change your mind, when I tell you that Moses told me that he finds it very hard to speak to you because of a bad odor that comes from your mouth." On hearing these words, the Caliph who had been walking down the court-room, stopped suddenly and turned pale. The Caliph was a simple, kind man and he was deeply hurt by Dijy's words. Flushing with anger, he commanded:

"Order Maimonides to come here at once and I will find out whether you are telling the truth, and woe to you if you are not."

Now that same morning the mean courtier had made sure to speak to Maimonides. To Maimonides the courtier had said:

"You think that because the Caliph has chosen you to be his physician, and maybe tells you how much he likes your books too, he really likes you. Well, let me tell you, you are all wrong. The other day he said to me, 'You know, Dijy, it's becoming quite impossible to speak to Maimonides; the odor from his mouth is so unpleasant.'" Maimonides who had listened attentively to Dijy's words, was deeply hurt.

Now when the Caliph sent for Maimonides that evening, Maimonides held a big handkerchief in front of his mouth so as not to annoy the Caliph. But the Caliph too had prepared for Maimonides' arrival, and he, too, had put a large handkerchief in front of his mouth.

When Maimonides entered, the Caliph thought: "Ah, so it's true! This Jew is two-faced. There he comes with his handkerchief over his nose." (The Caliph didn't notice that the handkerchief was over his mouth.) He grew angrier than ever.

Seeing the Caliph holding his handkerchief to his mouth, Moses' knees began to tremble so that he had to hold on to the furniture to keep from tottering. At last Moses reached the throne of the Caliph. The Caliph was so angry he could hardly speak. But he had already made his plans. So at last he said:

"You go to the outskirts of the city where they are burning lime in the big lime pit, and ask: 'Has the Caliph's bidding been carried out?'"

At another time Moses might have asked his friend, the Caliph, what he meant by such a peculiar question. But now, he felt altogether too embarrassed to say more than he had to.

The sun was setting, and it was getting dark. Many patients were waiting for Moses at his home. Nevertheless, without any complaint he turned to do the bidding of the Caliph.

Meanwhile the Caliph had sent a messenger to the head of the lime pit and ordered him to burn to death the man who would come within an hour and ask: "Has the Caliph's bidding been carried out?"

As Maimonides went on his way, he was met by an old woman who threw herself at his feet begging:

"Oh, please Doctor, please come in and see my daughter. She is dangerously sick, and only you can save her."

What was Maimonides to do? He had two duties to carry out. It was his duty to do the Caliph's bidding, but surely it was clearly his duty to save a human life. If he carried out the Caliph's command, the woman's daughter might die in the meantime. So what was he to do?

It did not take Moses long to make up his mind. He quickly turned to the woman and asked her to lead him to her home. There he gave the sick girl some medicine—and soon she was sleeping peacefully. Maimonides assured the mother that when her daughter awoke she would be on the road to health. This duty done, he went to the lime pit.

Meanwhile, the jealous courtier who had heard of the king's command to kill Moses, was very impatient.

He could not stay home, and await the good news of Maimonides' death. So, as the sun was setting, he hurriedly left for the lime pit. Upon his arrival he asked:

"Has the Caliph's bidding been carried out yet?"

When the lime burners heard the question they quickly fell on the courtier, tied him and threw him into the pit, where he was burnt to death.

A short while later, Maimonides, too, reached the pit and asked:

"Has the Caliph's command been carried out?"

With a smile and a twinkle in his eye, the head of the pit answered:

"Oh, yes, and a good job it was too." Saying no more, Moses turned homeward.

The following day Moses went to the court, as he always had done. As he approached the Caliph, Moses noticed that Saladin was pale and trembling.

"What is wrong, Your Majesty?" Moses asked greatly alarmed.

"Why didn't you go to the lime pit yesterday as I ordered you?" the Caliph asked, his eyes flashing with anger.

"I did, Your Majesty," Moses replied quietly. "And they told me that your bidding had been carried out, and that it had been a good job too."

"Oh, Allah, Allah!" the Caliph cried out. "A

poor innocent man must have been burnt alive—instead of you."

"Instead of me?" Moses called out in horror.

"Yes, I sent you to the lime pit yesterday to be burnt."

"You, Caliph,—me—to be burnt? Impossible! You wanted to kill me?" (Moses didn't know just what to say— He couldn't believe it all.) "Why, what evil have I done to Your Majesty?"

"Enough," said the Caliph. "You are not a true friend. If my mouth odor is truly bad, why couldn't you have told me instead of mocking me behind my back?"

A light dawned on Moses.

"Oh, was it Dijy who told you that?" he asked the Caliph.

"Yes, it was Dijy. If anyone else had told it to me, I wouldn't have believed him. But Dijy was your friend, and so I thought he was surely telling the truth. Then when I called for you, you came holding a handkerchief to your nose. How could I do anything but believe him? It was then that I made up my mind to kill you."

When Maimonides heard this he began to laugh. "Oh, that courtier is sly! You know, O Majesty, he told me the same about you. He said you told everybody that you wished you didn't have to speak to me so often, because you couldn't bear the odor from my mouth."

"Oh, how shameful," called the Caliph, who was really a kindhearted man. "To think that I was ready to believe him and take your life for that. Moses, can you forgive me?" The Caliph almost cried.

"Oh, I've forgotten about it already. Only I wonder who it was that met such a sad death at the lime pit." Moses was wrapped in thought.

"Moses," the Caliph cried, with great appreciation, "you are indeed the great philosopher, the great Moses Maimonides," and the Caliph embraced him affectionately.

Just then the Caliph's butler announced: "Two lime burners to see you, Your Majesty."

"Let them come in."

And the two lime burners came in holding a ring and a watch in their hands. The head of the lime burners spoke:

"We removed these things from the man whom you ordered to be burnt yesterday. Here, they belong to Your Majesty." As the men held them out, the Caliph exclaimed:

"Oh, these things belong to that jealous courtier who made me plan all that. He wanted to hear of your death and so he reached the pit before you did. By the way, Moses, where were you then?"

"Oh, God is good," Moses smiled. "An old lady came and asked me to heal her sick daughter. I hope Your Majesty will pardon me, I stopped to attend the sick girl before going to the lime pit, because I feared that she might die if I did not go immediately."

"Oh, how impossible it is for us to understand the ways of God!" the Caliph exclaimed. Again they embraced each other, and Moses and the Caliph remained friends for the rest of their lives.

THE RABBI WINS

"IN THE name of the Lord of Hosts,—I come, I come in the name of the Lord of Hosts!"

This was the cry of Pablo Christiani as he went through Spain, from city to city. Pablo was a Jew who had become a Christian. And now he wanted all the Jews to do the same. But try as he would, he could not succeed.

One day Pablo thought of a new scheme. He requested the king to have one of the most famous rabbis in Spain debate with him. That is, Pablo wanted to argue with the rabbi as to which was the better religion, Judaism or Christianity. The king was glad to grant Pablo's wish for he too wanted to see the Jews turn Christian.

Pablo thought: "It will be very easy for me to show that Christianity is the better religion. The rabbi will be afraid to argue honestly before the king. He will have to agree to whatever I say. Then, once I shall have shown the people that even their own great rabbi agrees that Christianity is the better religion, my work will be done; the Jews will all consent to become Christians."

Now the greatest rabbi in Spain at that time was Moses ben Nachman or Nachmanides, as he was called. When the king asked him to appear in Barcelona for the debate, Nachmanides was worried. Just what was he to do? Just what ought he to say?

"Anyway," Nachmanides thought to himself, "no matter what I do and no matter what I say, the Jews will suffer. It's best that I speak the truth—nothing but the truth."

So with great fear and yet also with great hope, Nachmanides arrived in Barcelona. When he came into the palace he found it crowded with many Jews and Christians who had gathered to hear the great debate. The Jews of Spain, however, were not the only ones interested in this debate. The Jews all over the world were worried. What would happen to them now, they wondered. Wasn't this another trick of the king's? Would this not give him another excuse to be cruel to the Jews? Still they put great trust in Nachmanides, their rabbi.

When all were seated and waiting impatiently,

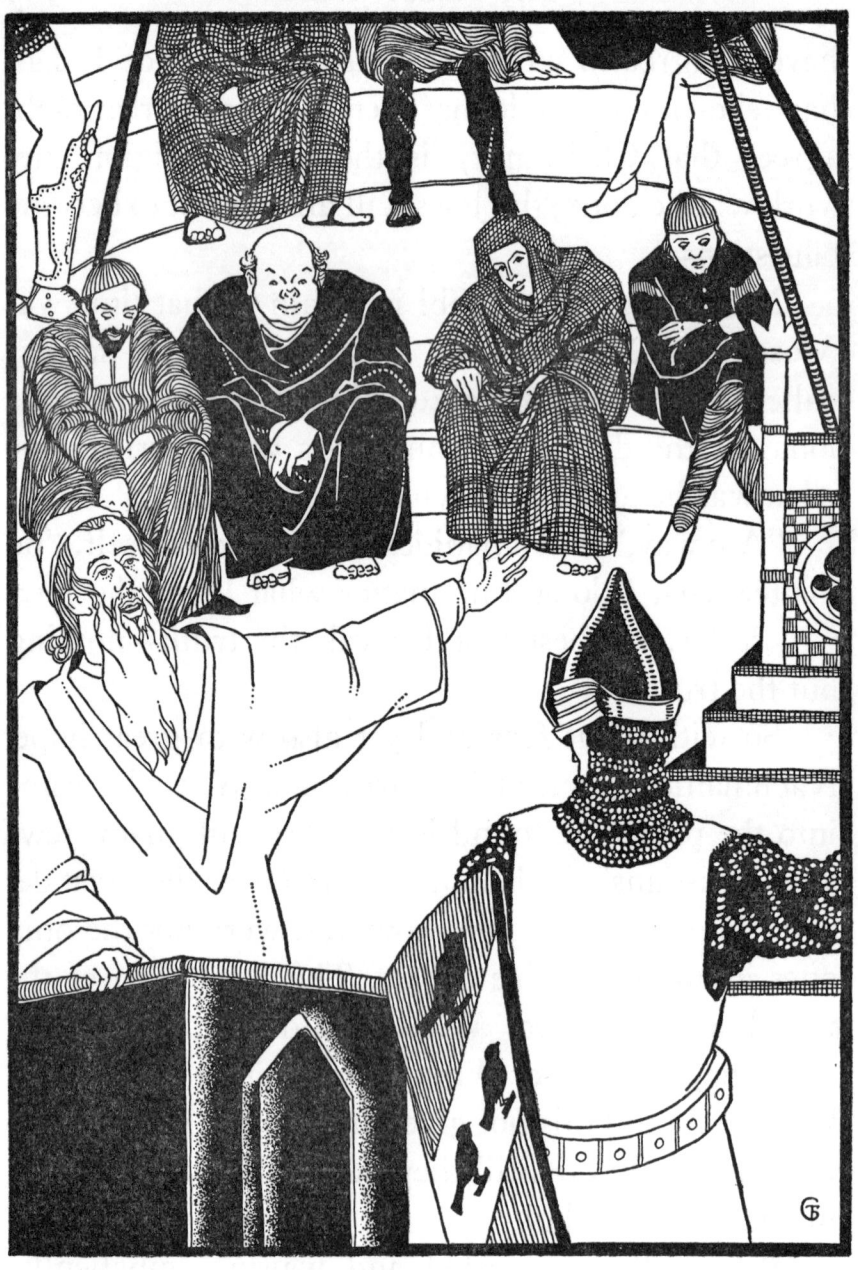

Nachmanides arose, and addressed the people as follows:

"Before beginning the debate, I ask for one thing." Everybody craned his neck. Everybody strained his ears to hear what Nachmanides was asking for.

"All I ask is that I be allowed to speak the truth, the truth as I see it," Nachmanides begged.

"Of course, of course. That is what we expect of both you and Pablo," the king answered in his courtly manner.

For three days the debate went on. Nachmanides spoke without fear. "It surely cannot be that the Messiah has come. Was it not said that when the Messiah came all wars would end, and there would be peace, only peace on this earth? But look, look about you! What do you see—nothing but war and bloodshed. Surely Jesus was not the Messiah."

"That's so! That's really true!" Many who were listening to Nachmanides thought to themselves. But they dared not applaud such ideas.

"What? Jesus not a Messiah! The Messiah had not yet come! That rabbi had better stop debating before he is killed."

The Jews and even some of the Christians begged Nachmanides not to continue the debate. But Nachmanides paid no attention to their requests. He went right on arguing bravely.

At last the debate was over. Pablo had not been able, as he expected, to show everybody that Christianity was a better religion than Judaism. Nachmanides had not been afraid to speak the truth, as Pablo had hoped. There was no doubt that the great rabbi had won the debate.

Nachmanides wrote down the whole story of the debate. He sent it all over the country, so the Jews and the Christians could read all that had been said.

Now when Pablo and the priests saw the report, they selected certain sentences and sent them to the king. Why do you suppose they did this? Well, you see they took those sentences which belittled the Christian religion. For example, one sentence read, "There have been more wars since Jesus was born, than there had ever been before." Another read, "Jesus is not the Messiah" and other sentences like these.

These wicked men came before the king and said:

"Words like these are an insult to our Christian religion. The man who wrote them surely ought not to go unpunished."

Again Nachmanides was summoned to Barcelona. Greatly alarmed, he obeyed the king's order.

"Nachmanides," said the king, "it gives me much

pain to inform you that you have been charged with insulting the Christian religion. Pablo showed me the report you made of the meeting in Barcelona."

"What? What was that?" asked Nachmanides, who was now seventy years old. Maybe he hadn't heard the king correctly.

"Yes, yes," the king continued, "and for that sin you must leave the country for two years."

Nachmanides turned very pale. He sank into a chair exhausted.

"But how did this happen, Your Majesty?" he asked. "I didn't write anything in that report which I hadn't already spoken before you, O Majesty! You don't really mean to make me leave my home, my wife, my children, and my little grandchildren, whom I love so much," Nachmanides pleaded in a voice choked with tears.

The cruel king sat by unmoved. "Yes, Nachmanides, that shall have to be," he replied sternly. "The pope has spoken! For two years you shall stay away from this country."

"Two years," cried the clergy. "That is not enough punishment for a crime like that. For the rest of his life, let him be a wanderer on the earth!"

A great sob arose from some of the women present. A grey old man of seventy to be forced to leave his home, his son and daughter, and his little grandchildren. That was unheard of.

So Nachmanides began his wanderings through Europe. After three years of weary travels, he came to Palestine where at last he found peace. From there he wrote to one of his friends:

"I am removed from my friends and my family, from the little children whom I brought up on my knee, but I feel repaid when I can walk on the stones of Jerusalem and weep at Jerusalem's fallen Temple."

Although at first Nachmanides was disappointed when he saw the ruins of the once beautiful city, he didn't sit and mourn over those ruins. Instead Nachmanides, brave man that he was, gathered about him a small group of friends. He encouraged them to build up a real community. Many came to hear his lectures and sermons. And so Nachmanides was able to give the Jews of the Holy Land all the fine culture of Spain. Nachmanides lived in Palestine only three years. But he did more in those three years than others do in a whole lifetime.

NOT FOR HIS CROWN

Rashi's father lived in a small town in France, near the sea. He was very poor, and he had to work very hard, loading and unloading the boats. One day as he was walking near the harbor, he thought he saw something very bright in the dirty sand. He stopped, and sure enough there, between two little pebbles, lay a very precious pearl.

Hardly believing his eyes, Reb Isaac picked up the jewel and ran home. His wife, Sarah, when she saw him running towards the house, became worried. What could have happened? Why was Isaac coming home so early? And why was he running? In her great anxiety, Rashi's mother began to run towards her husband.

"Look! Look, Sarah!" called Isaac all out of breath. "See," he said between gasps, "see, I just found this pearl at the harbor."

"Isaac!" cried his wife with joy, "you'll never have to carry those heavy loads again."

"And I shall be able to sit and study the Torah all the time. Just think of that!" replied Isaac, his eyes filling with tears.

"I shall take it to the jeweler immediately," said Sarah as Isaac carefully handed her the jewel.

With trembling hands and a very fast beating heart, Sarah ran into the store of the jeweler.

"Look at this pearl. Isn't it very, very precious indeed?" she asked tremblingly.

The jeweler examined it carefully with his magnifying glass. (You know that's a glass that makes everything look much, much bigger than it really is.) He held the pearl up to the sun and then again in front of his candle.

"Yes, yes," the jeweler at last said slowly, as if talking to himself. "This jewel is worth a lot. I will give you 10,000 ducats for it."

Now it happened that on that very day, the jeweler had received an order from the bishop for a very expensive jewel, one that would be fit to set in his crown. So the jeweler was very anxious to buy this pearl from Rashi's mother.

"Yes," the jeweler said again, "I need this pearl to adorn the bishop's crown, and even though it's not worth 10,000 ducats, I will pay you that much so that I may have it for the bishop's crown."

"Oh, is it that bishop who hates the Jews? That bishop who wants all the Jews to become Christians?"

The jeweler continued to examine the pearl, as if he hadn't heard what Sarah had said.

"Is that the bishop?" Sarah asked again.

Looking up, the jeweler smiled and said: "Well, I guess he is the one you mean."

Without saying another word, Sarah took the jewel from him and carefully wrapped it up. The jeweler watched her, wondering what she was going to do next. As he saw her turn to walk out, he said:

"What's the matter, woman, don't you think 10,000 is enough for that pearl?"

"Oh, indeed, more than enough, I'm sure, but I must go home to ask my husband's advice."

Do you think Sarah was foolish for not selling the pearl to the jeweler immediately? Do you know why she didn't sell the jewel?

Just listen to what happened. Sarah came home and told her husband the whole story. So he said:

"Well, Sarah, you didn't sell the jewel to him, did you?"

"Why, how did you guess?" asked Sarah wonderingly.

"Because I know you wouldn't want to have your jewel adorn the crown of a wicked man."

"That's it exactly. I was hoping you wouldn't be angry with me," Sarah answered smilingly.

"No, no, far from it," and with those words Isaac took the jewel from his wife's hands and threw it into the sea.

"I would rather the sea had it, than that it should adorn that man's crown," he said.

Now if this was the kind of people Rashi's parents were, what would you expect of their son? And what might have happened, had Isaac and Sarah kept the jewel? Think of that!

HOW RASHI WAS SAVED

"AND so, my dear Brethren of Prague, I want to tell you that the Jews are getting on very nicely in France. They are not as rich as our Spanish brethren, nor are they allowed to take part in the government as the Jews of Spain are, but they keep on studying the Bible and the Talmud. And they continue to have great schools like those in Babylonia.

"Thank you, my friends, thank you for giving me such a big gift. Because of that I shall not have to work for the rest of my life. But I don't think that it is right. I believe a rabbi should earn a living by the work of his hands, and no rabbi should receive money for serving his people.

"I want to thank you again for the fine way in which you have welcomed me to your city." With these words Rabbi Rashi ended his talk.

"Oh, what we have done does not begin to show

you how much we appreciate the fine things you have written for us, and for our children after us. You have made the Bible so clear that our children will now be able to read it," answered the spokesman of the congregation.

Rashi was about to say something, when suddenly officers rushed into the synagogue and taking hold of him, said:

"By the order of the duke, you are arrested!" A few of the elders of the synagogue became very angry and excited, and rushed up to the platform.

"Arrested?" they cried. "What for?"

"This man is a spy. He came to find out which parts of the land can be easily attacked."

Rashi turned to the elders of the synagogue and said:

"Don't grieve, my dear friends. Nothing can happen to me, because I'm not guilty. Wait for the trial and trust in God." So Rashi was imprisoned for four days.

At last the day of the trial came. Rashi was brought before the duke.

"Are you the great Jewish scholar, the one whom the Jews have so honored?" the duke asked angrily.

"Yes, they gave me a very fine welcome," said Rashi modestly.

"Then you are the spy. And you shall surely be hanged."

During this time, the bishop, who was the chief judge, sat by looking very closely at Rashi. It seemed to him he had seen this man somewhere before, but he couldn't remember just where it had been. Little by little, however, it came back to him. This man was a rabbi, a great scholar.

"Oh, yes, yes, to be sure!" Suddenly he turned to Rashi and asked:

"Were you ever in Palestine?"

"Yes, I travel from country to country, trying to learn everywhere," answered Rashi. At the same time, Rashi also recognized the bishop.

The bishop then turned to the duke and said:

"Let no harm be done to this man. Neither shall he be put into prison, for I know that not only is he a great and learned rabbi, but he is also a very fine man. Let me tell you how I know this:

"Sometime ago when I was in Palestine, there was a learned Jew at the inn where I had stopped. When I heard that, I asked to be introduced to the learned rabbi. We sat together, and talked about religion. Rashi told me about his work, and his teachings. He told me that he was trying to continue the worthy work that had been done in Palestine and in Babylonia by the many great rabbis who came before him.

"That same night I suddenly became very sick. And this rabbi, this Jewish man, sat up with me all that night and the whole day after that and the whole night after that, and prepared medicines for me, which he knew would help to cure me. But for this man I might have been dead now. When I was better and he was leaving the inn, I begged him to accept some money or at least some little gift for all his kind services. But with many thanks he refused and said:

"'You are not a Jew. You are not of my religion. But you were sick and I did the best I could for you. Now, all I ask is that if ever you meet a Jew who is in trouble you do all you can for him.' And Rashi shook hands with me and left.

"And do you know, O duke, this man standing before us now is no spy. He is the great rabbi who saved my life. Now then, can I do anything less for him than beg that you grant him his freedom?"

And so all the Jews rejoiced, for Rashi was allowed to return to his native France.

THE FOURTH HORSE

"GODFREY of Bouillon has ordered you to come before him," the soldiers of Godfrey commanded. But Rashi refused to go. So the soldiers returned and reported this to Godfrey. Godfrey was greatly upset by this, but nevertheless he thought:

"I guess that little rabbi is afraid of me. I will go down myself and make him feel sure that I mean no harm."

When Godfrey came to Rashi's school, he went right into the school, for all the doors were open. He walked in expecting, of course, to find someone there. But to his great surprise, though every door was open, he saw no one.

Can you guess what had happened? As soon as Godfrey came in, Rashi, through his magic power, had made himself invisible.

Godfrey walked first into one room, then into an-

other room until he had gone through the whole school building. He couldn't believe that Rashi would be so foolish as to leave all the doors open and go away. At last, after he had looked all over, he called out:

"Rashi, are you anywhere in the building? Rashi, Rashi. This is Godfrey of Bouillon calling you. Do you hear me?" To his great astonishment, Godfrey heard a voice answer:

"Here I am. What does my master want?" Godfrey turned and looked all over the room. He rubbed his eyes again and again to make sure that he was seeing straight. He became frightened, for he surely did not see anybody in the room.

"What's this?" he called out angrily. "Is some devil making fun of me?" And again Godfrey called:

"Rashi, where are you? Do you know that this is Godfrey of Bouillon calling you? Then what is this joke you are trying to play on me?"

But again a voice answered from nowhere, "Here I am. What is it my master wants?"

By now Godfrey was so angry that he went out of the school and started homeward. At the same time, he made up his mind that if he ever found Rashi he would kill him.

No sooner had Godfrey left the school than he met one of Rashi's pupils.

"Please go and tell your teacher to come before me. Surely no harm shall come to him."

When Rashi was sure that Godfrey meant no harm, he came and stood before Godfrey.

"You are a great scholar, Rashi, and every one has heard of your wisdom. Can you tell me then, whether I shall be victorious on this crusade which I am about to begin? Tell me truthfully, for you will surely not be punished for whatever you say."

After a pause Rashi answered slowly, "You will capture the city of Jerusalem and you will be king over Jerusalem for three days, but on the fourth day the Moslems will put you to flight. And when you come back, you will be left with only three horses."

At this announcement, Godfrey became red with anger. This was so different from the glorious victory he had planned.

When his anger passed so that he could speak again, he said:

"If this does come true, and if I return with only one more horse than you say, your body will be thrown to the dogs, and all the Jews of France will be killed."

For a number of years Godfrey was fighting in Jerusalem. When he returned to France he had three soldiers with him, just as Rashi had said, but four horses instead of three. Godfrey was, of course, very angry and disappointed. He had not succeeded in capturing Jerusalem and remaining there, as he had hoped, and so he was angry with the world. With a mean glare in his eyes, he was thinking:

"Four horses, that is one more than three, and I will take my revenge on that Rashi!"

Just as Godfrey was entering Troyes, the city where Rashi lived, a large rock from the heavy gate dislodged itself and fell upon one of the soldiers. And lo, both the soldier and his horse were killed. And so Godfrey was left with only three horses just as Rashi had told him before.

"A miracle, a miracle!" called out Godfrey, who was quite beside himself. "The prophecy of Rashi is fulfilled!"

FLYING FROM THE ROOFS

"Jews of Asia, hear ye! How long will you agree to be trodden under the heel of the Mohammedans? The Jewish people must do something real, something worth while. We can do that only in our own country, Palestine. So join yourselves with me in this great undertaking. Onward! Onward to the Holy Land!" Thus spoke David Alroy, a dark, handsome young man. David knew the Bible and the Talmud well and also the Arabic language.

"Hear ye, my fellow Jews," continued David, "the Lord has sent me to you to take you out of the land of the Mohammedans, into our own holy city, Jerusalem. In order to do this I need your help to fight the other nations. In the name of the God of Israel, then, join my great army. Come to Amadia and take with you under your coats as many swords and spears as you can carry. Make sure that no one sees your weapons, and let no one have the least notion that you are hiding weapons."

"Yea! Yea! Hail to the Messiah! Hail to David, the Messiah!"

The Jews were suffering so much because of the terrible crusades, that they were glad to listen to anybody who promised to lead them away from their sufferings. And didn't David Alroy say himself, that God had sent him?

When the Sultan heard rumors of the arrival of a Jewish Messiah, he ordered that that Messiah be brought before him. And when David, the supposed Messiah, did appear before the Sultan, he was ordered to be put into prison.

Just as the Sultan was thinking of a severe enough punishment for David and his followers, David suddenly, to the great astonishment of all, appeared before the Sultan and said:

> "*By magic arts*
> *I come and go,*
> *By magic arts*
> *I swim,*
> *By magic arts*
> *I roam on high*
> *And all of you defy.*"

"Seize him! Seize him!" ordered the Sultan. And the guards laid hold on Alroy but, again, to their great bewilderment they clasped air, thin air. David suddenly made himself invisible, and in that way crossed a big river. In one day David was back again in Amadia. It would have taken an ordinary man at least ten days to get there.

By this time the fame of David Alroy had spread into many countries. In one of these countries there lived two wicked men. These men saw a way of getting rich through David Alroy, and this is what they did.

They wrote letters to the Jews of Bagdad. And they made believe that the letters had been written by David Alroy. In these letters they told the Jews that they should all prepare for Monday night. On that Monday night they were going to be delivered. And how? By flying away to Jerusalem.

"Dress yourselves in green robes. Go up to the roof and wait. Wait for the hour at which you will begin to fly." And the letter was signed "David Alroy."

The Jews had such a firm belief in David, their Messiah, that they thought anything could happen if only he promised it. So these Jews, thinking they would fly to Jerusalem, handed over all their belongings to these wicked men.

At last the promised Monday night came. Crowds of Jews gathered on the roofs. Everybody was excited. The children shouted with joy, while the elders wept with happiness. Everybody was on edge. Think of it! They would fly—and not in an airplane. But just like birds they would let themselves go and fly, fly to Jerusalem.

Hour after hour passed. Each one looked at his neighbor to make sure that all would begin to fly at the same time, or maybe to see who would go off first. With great hope which later turned into anxiety they waited. One and two hours passed. No. No one had begun to fly, not yet. Three and four hours passed. Even the staunchest believers were getting impatient.

The sun was already beginning to rise. Their confidence began to weaken. Some began to wonder a little. How did they know that David had written the letters? How could they be sure?

Some of the people were quite chilled by the morning air. And some children had fallen asleep in spite of their great interest.

Daybreak at last! Now it became clear to them. Where were those two men who had read the letter to them? What had they done with all the things that had been given them? Where had those men gone? It did not take them long to discover that it was all a fraud.

Flying from the Roofs

They began to rush down from the roofs just as hurriedly as they had come up. Like crazy people they rushed down and into their houses. But, alas! Those two wicked men had already done their work. Every house had been cleared of all of its belongings. And the two men were far, far away, out of anybody's reach.

But you see, the Jews' hope for a Messiah, a redeemer, someone who would save them from all their sufferings was so great that they had believed anything possible. They had never thought that those two men were just two wicked people.

Ever after the people of Bagdad called that the "year of flying" and counted their calendar from that time. And though David Alroy knew nothing about the letter the two wicked men had written, he was one of the many false Messiahs.

THE MESSIAH IS COMING

THE Jews were being driven from country to country. In no land were they welcome. In no land could they feel safe. Because of this, many Jews began to hope and yearn for a redeemer to take them out of their trouble. Many longed for this redeemer so much that they began to think that they themselves were sent down to redeem Israel! Others, seeing how anxious the Jews were for a savior, thought it a good chance for them to act as such. Just what Abraham Abulafia believed we cannot tell, but this is what he did. Abulafia went about preaching thus:

"All of you who want to be saved, all you who wish to be happy, shut yourselves up in a quiet room. Shut yourselves away from the world. Clothe yourselves in white garments. Wrap yourselves in a *talith* and *tefillin,* and in that way prepare yourselves for the Lord.

"Besides, if you would indeed have the Lord come to you then pronounce the name of God every few minutes, '*Je-ho-vah, Je-ho-vah,*' and keep changing your voice as you do so. And as you do all these things, sway, sway back and forth. Then your head will become dizzy, and your heart filled with a glow. Suddenly, sleep will come over you, and you will feel as if the soul were going out of your body. In this way will the Lord come to you."

Abulafia traveled from country to country preaching his strange idea to all whom he met. Little by little he began to believe that he himself was the Messiah. And many people believed him also. He wrote books explaining just when and how the Messiah would arrive. He also set the date when the Messiah would come.

The people prepared for the great day. To make sure that they would be allowed to go along with the Messiah, they gave a great deal to the poor and they fasted. On the day set, the people dressed themselves in long white garments, as on the Day of Atonement, ran to the synagogue and waited there for the long, loud note of the *Shofar,* the trumpet blast by which the Messiah would be announced.

They waited and waited, but no blast was heard. Suddenly they looked about. What do you think they saw? Some fainted at the sight that met their eyes. On their garments were little, tiny crosses. What could this mean? How did these crosses get there?

At first, great fear and alarm came over the people. Little by little, however, they began to see how foolish they had been. To believe in such silly things, to imagine that such stupid fasting and almost crazy screeching would call down the Messiah! Of course, some one had played a trick on them. When they had not been looking, the crosses had been pinned on to their hems to frighten them. Though still disappointed that the Messiah had not arrived, they returned home with clearer heads. No one would again deceive them about the Messiah. But would no one?

SO THIS IS YOUR ANSWER

IN ONE of the crowded streets of the city of Worms a priest was speaking to a large gathering of people. All were listening with great interest when suddenly a child called to his mother:

"Look, Mother, look at that man walking towards the priest. How dusty and torn his clothes are! He looks tired, too. And, see, Mother, he has a pilgrim's staff in his hand. I wonder from where he comes!"

Before his mother could reply, the man had walked up to the priest and cried aloud in a trembling voice:

"Hear ye, brethren, I have just returned from the Holy Land. When I first came there with my companions, we wanted to visit the grave of Jesus. But when we came near it, we found it surrounded by hundreds of infidels who would not let us see it. You who live quietly and peacefully here, cannot imagine all we pilgrims had to suffer near that holy grave. This ought not to continue any longer. We must rescue it from the hands of those infidels."

"That's right, that's right," shouted the people.

Then the priest called loudly: "All those who want to go to the Holy Land to fight for the grave of Jesus, gather here!"

Some hundreds of people, not only in Worms but in other cities, too, formed themselves into bands and started on the pilgrimage to the Holy Land. They put a little red cross on their cloaks and so they were called crusaders. In order to get many men to go on these crusades to the Holy Grave, the popes sent out proclamations, called bulls, in which they said:

"Let it be known that all men who join in this holy war, in this crusade against the unbelievers in Jerusalem,—let it be known that the sins of these crusaders will be forgiven, and they will be excused from paying all their debts."

Now it happened that in those days many Christians owed money to the Jews. When they heard the pope's bull, they thought:

"Now we can get even with those Jews! We won't pay our debts and they will not be able to take us to court either." And they were very happy.

There were also monks and priests who for many, many years had tried to get the Jews to become Christians. These monks said: "Before going to Palestine to fight the unbelievers there, why not begin with the unbelievers right here?" So it came about that the crusaders while traveling to the Holy Land turned upon the Jews in the cities of Europe, whom they called infidels, and attacked them.

Since the popes in their bulls forgave all sins and excused all debts, many bad people, such as thieves and robbers, joined the crusades. When crusaders of this kind came through Jewish towns, they began to break into Jewish homes.

In Worms, when the Jews heard that the crusaders had come, they rushed to the bishop's castle. The bishop was a kind man and they were sure he would protect them.

The crusaders ran from house to house and from synagogue to synagogue. Furious because they found no one, they determined to destroy everything belonging to the Jews. First they tore the holy books and the Torah; then they set fire to the houses and synagogues. Still their anger was unsatisfied. And so they stormed the bishop's castle, crying madly: "Hand over those infidels! If they want to live they must become Christians."

When the bishop, who was in one of his rooms in the castle, heard this, he came forward and pleaded with the crusaders:

"What good will it do to Christianity if many Jews, who really don't want to become Christians, will make believe they are Christians?"

But the crazed mob would not listen. "We want those Jews!" they shouted.

The bishop, seeing he could no longer resist the mob which was growing wilder all the time, came to the Jews and told them that he could not protect them any longer.

"You must be baptized," he said, "or these men will compel me to hand you over to them."

Can you imagine how the Jews felt? What were they to do? Shalom, chief among the Jews, begged:

"Please give us just one hour in which to consider whether we shall die as Jews or live as Christians."

"Very well," said the bishop, "I shall try to keep away this mad mob for another hour. But remember, do not hold me responsible after that."

Yes, the Jews had only one hour in which to decide between life and death. During that hour the mad mob kept on battering away at the castle doors.

"We are giving those unbelievers too much time. Out with them! Death upon them!"

Meanwhile, what had the Jews decided? Do you think you can guess? Let us see.

Some, a very few, said: "Oh, suppose we are baptized, suppose we do say those words: 'In the name of the Father, the Son and the Holy Ghost, we are baptized,' and then let them sprinkle a few drops of water on us! When we are free, we will become Jews again."

"No, no, we will never listen to that," the others cried.

They considered this way out and that way out. At last they made their decision. At the end of the hour, when the bishop returned, he was stunned at the sight which met his eyes. There lay the Jews—dead. They had chosen to kill themselves rather than to give up their religion.

"So," said the bishop, as a shudder went through him. "So this is your answer."

And the Jews all over the world remember and honor these men of Worms as "Kedoshim," holy ones, saints, who were strong enough to die for their religion!

WHITHER—NOW?

*"Granada has fallen
Gone are the Moors—
Gone are these infidels
Why not the Jews?"*

So chanted the crowds as Ferdinand and Isabella marched victoriously into Granada. Banners were waving; bells were ringing; people were shouting: "Down with the Moors! Down with the Jews!" And soon a proclamation was sent throughout the whole of Spain which read:

"By the thirteenth of July not a Jew shall be found in any part of Spain."

"Have you heard the proclamation?" Don Caesar, a very rich Jew, asked Don Pedro.

"Which proclamation?" Don Pedro asked, rather ashamed that he wasn't keeping up with the times.

"Don't you know that in four months we Jews shall have to leave Spain?" Don Caesar replied.

"Oh, I can't believe it. It isn't possible. It can't be true. Don't Ferdinand and Isabella know that Halevi, Ibn Gabirol, Maimonides, and Ibn Ezra were all Jews? Don't they know that their greatest philosophers and poets were Jews? What can the King and Queen be thinking of?" Don Pedro was getting more and more excited.

"Why, our ablest financiers, our greatest business men are Jews. Even at this very moment Isaac Abravanel, a Jew, is holding a very high position at the court," added Don Caesar.

But in a few days the King's messengers were calling throughout the land:

"Jews! Hear ye. All you who do not accept Christianity must leave this realm—or die."

Now, only one who has lived in Spain knows how beautiful that country is. Only one who has lived in Spain knows how difficult it is to leave it. The Jews had lived there for hundreds of years. They had made Spain rich, and, as a result, they themselves had become rich. They loved the country and they could not bear to leave it now. Over and over again they said to one another:

"We shall not go. We shall refuse to leave!"

Don Caesar Arobio and Don Pedro were chosen to write a letter to Abravanel, who was at the court. Don Caesar and Don Pedro ended the letter with these words: "Don Abravanel, you have power. You know how much the Jews have done for Spain. You know how they hate to leave it. Our fate is in your hands. You must appeal to the King and Queen. We look to you to save us!"

What could Abravanel do? He was sorry for his brother Jews. He tried to argue and plead with the King, but it did not help. At last Abravanel took money, hundreds, thousands, even millions of ducats and heaped up great piles of gold before the King. Abravanel knew that the King liked money more than anything in the world, better than his religion, and better even than his God.

At the sight of the money Ferdinand softened. He began to smile and asked:

"Perhaps; but how much will you pay?"

"You can set your own price," said Abravanel.

Ferdinand was about to answer when in walked the cruel Torquemada, one of the heads of the Catholic Church.

"Will you sell the Church for money?" he shouted. "Remember, the curse of the Church will fall on your head."

Whither—Now?

Everyone feared Torquemada, even the King himself. This decided it for Ferdinand.

"I'm sorry, Abravanel," he said to his Jewish financier, "the Jews must leave Spain. And neither gold nor silver will they be allowed to take with them." Then in a low tone he said to Abravanel:

"Of course, Abravanel, you are welcome to stay here as long as you live." Abravanel bowed and politely said:

"Thank you, we shall see about that later."

Soon the date for the expulsion came. It happened to be the ninth of Ab, the same day on which the Temple in Jerusalem had fallen. Long and loud was the wailing of the Jews. Not only were they being driven out of their beloved country, but they were being sent away penniless. They were not allowed to take gold or silver with them, so they had to exchange their belongings for almost nothing. For many acres of land they had to accept a few sheep; for their beautiful houses, a few horses.

Left without a home, without a country, without their wealth, old and young had to go. Some were sick and some were dying of grief. But Torquemada did not want Spain to be filled with "unbelievers." So the Jews had to go.

Many were robbed and murdered on the sea.

Whither—Now?

Many never lived to see the land to which they were fleeing for protection. Some were captured by sea vessels, and when they had no money to give to the captain they were thrown into the sea. Others, who were allowed to live, were sold as slaves.

And where were they going? One group with Isaac Abravanel as its leader went to Italy, for you surely did not think that Abravanel would remain in Spain, while his brother Jews were driven to strange lands. Abravanel was very famous, not only in Spain but also in many other countries of Europe. So he and the group of Jews who went with him were welcomed in Italy.

Some Jews went to Africa, and still others went to Turkey. Many were sold as slaves, and parents had to be separated from their children.

And so Spain was cleared of her Jews. But at the same time that the Jews were driven from Spain, Columbus started on his voyage to East India. The Jews had given their money not knowing that it would help Columbus discover a new land—a land of refuge for all the suffering Jews, as well as for other people. Into this land the Jews would bring their Bible and their Talmud. Forgetting their troubles, they would carry over their high ideals, and live on as a great people for centuries to come.

Now Spain became less and less important, while this new land, which granted religious freedom to its people, became one of the greatest countries in the world. Some day we shall see how the Jews came to America and how they lived in this new land of freedom.